HAUNTED
LIVERPOOL 15

For Mark Simmo

© Tom Slemen 2007

Published by The Bluecoat Press, Liverpool
Book design by March Graphic Design Studio, Liverpool
Printed by Ashford Colour Press

ISBN 1 904438 65 2

Tom Slemen

HAUNTED
LIVERPOOL 15

The Bluecoat Press

CONTENTS

INTRODUCTION

People have often said to me, "Ghosts don't exist; it's common sense. Once you're dead you're dead. No one can escape from the grave," even though a number of these people have been self-professed Christians. The entire Christian faith is based on a belief in a man who left his tomb days after suffering an horrific death. As for common sense; didn't common sense once tell us that the sun moved around the earth, and that the earth was flat? Isaac Newton's common sense told him that space and time were the same everywhere – until Einstein proved him wrong.

Common sense is fallible, and many of our suppositions are based on erroneous information. For example, I once heard a man in pub say a person that he knew "drank like a dolphin". In fact, dolphins don't drink; they obtain their water by burning up their body fat. Another common quip I have often heard is, "When Nelson gets his eye back" meaning, if that can happen, anything can. In fact, Admiral Nelson had two eyes. His right one was damaged, yet he was still able to see with it. At school I was taught that water will always spiral in a clockwise direction as it goes down the plughole, unless I were in the southern hemisphere, because of the Corilolis Force – but in reality that force is too weak to influence the way in which water turns as it goes down a plughole.

Even common sense notions about the food we eat are often wrong. I, like many people, used to assume that chicken tikka masala was a dish which had originated in India, whereas it was actually invented in Glasgow, around 1966. Chicken tikka is, without question, a traditional Bangladeshi dish, but the masala is the mixture of spices, which were later added to the dish in Scotland of all places! There is no limit to the depth of our ignorance. When I was at school I innocently asked if bananas grew on trees, but the teacher was not sure, and nor was the headmaster. No one seemed to know for certain, but most people assumed that there must be such a thing as a banana tree – but no such thing exists. Bananas are actually the product of a herb.

One night in the 1950s, a Liverpool man by the name of Wright was ridiculed by his mates in the pub when he stated that he had cracked open a block of coal (taken from Martindale's Coal Yard on Crown Street) and a live toad had jumped out. There were guffaws of laughter in the Spekeland Castle public house when he showed people the two halves of the coal lump in which he had found the living toad. Everyone said that he was a liar, yet, for centuries, toads and frogs have been found alive in such curious circumstances and no one is able to say how they do it. One of these frogs was even put on show at the Great Exhibition of London, in 1862. The lump of coal bore the distinct impression of the frog and both it and the frog's body were set out in a glass case for all to see. The amphibian had been discovered in a lump of coal that had been unearthed in a colliery at Newport, Monmouthshire.

In 1825, Dr Frank Buckland decided to get to the bottom of the toad-in-the-hole 'myth' by encasing twelve toads in blocks of limestone and sandstone, which he sealed with putty and covered with glass and slate. The twelve toads were then buried three feet down in the doctor's own garden. A year later the toads were dug up, and all the ones encased in limestone were dead and shrivelled up, but most of the toads that had been entombed in sandstone were not only alive, but some had even put on weight during their enforced hibernation. A few sceptics argued that tiny insects must have crawled into the blocks to keep them alive, but such bugs would have needed to get through putty, glass and slate, which would clearly have been impossible. As far as I know, no one has done research on toad survival in coal.

Haunted Liverpool 15 is all about those unusual and often inexplicable things, which are often outside our everyday experience, and they make a mockery of common sense, just as quantum physics does. No one currently understands the Laws of Nature at their most fundamental level, but a growing number of physicists are beginning to suspect that someone wrote the laws – a Grand Architect, a Superior Being, or God, call it what you will. In a letter to a friend, Einstein once wrote: "Quantum mechanics is certainly imposing. But an inner voice tells me that it is not yet the real thing. The theory says a lot, but does not really bring us any closer to the secret of the Old One."

The Old One must have created the Universe, whether you believe in the Big Bang theory or not. After all, isn't the Big Bang theory a mystical, unfathomable puzzle, indistinguishable from a mysterious God saying, "Let there be light"?

The greatest obstacle to discovery is not ignorance, but the illusion of knowledge. When we die we may well continue in some form, in some place, but just because we don't have sufficient information on the post-death state, we should not assume that death is the end. That would be the equivalent of believing that the sun has gone forever after it has sunk below the horizon. Studies in near-death-experiences have shown that people with no detectable electrical activity in their brains after 'death', have somehow seen their own physical bodies lying inert on hospital beds and operating tables. After being resuscitated and brought back to life, they have talked about grand vistas of light and colour, and of meeting deceased loved ones; all things that ought to be impossible when no electrical activity is going on in the brain. It is as if the brain were merely some 'eye' that feeds the mind, and the mind is not contained in a physical place.

Common sense is fine most of the time and helps us cope with the mundane things in everyday life, but it cannot, and should not, be applied to everything in the universe.

OUR WORLD

Even today, there are still places on the surface of this planet which are not accurately represented on any maps. The following unusual tale illustrates this phenomenum perfectly.

In 1901, two English ladies, Anne Moberley and Eleanor Jourdain – visited the Palace of Versailles in France, and during their visit, they decided to go in search of the Petit Trianon, a small château located in the grounds of the Palace and originally built for the mistress of King Louis XV, Madame de Pompadour. Alas, Madame de Pompadour died four years before the château was completed, and so a twenty-year-old King Louis XVI gave the beautiful building to his queen, Marie Antoinette. Marie would often retreat to the Petit Trianon when court life became too wearisome, and she would only allow a close inner circle of her friends to visit her there – and circle was so exclusive that it did not even include the king!

Anyway, on that warm and sunny afternoon in August 1901, the two Misses Moberley and Jourdain went in search of the Petit Trianon. They found it, but it wasn't the twentieth century manifestation, but the château exactly how it was in the days of the French Revolution. Fascinated, the two women set off on a tour of the gardens of the Petit Trianon and found it to be exactly as it had been over a century before. Not only did they meet several people from that era, they even caught a glimpse of Marie Antoinette herself, hiding in the shrubbery. Later, when the two women compared notes, they realised they had witnessed the fateful events of 10 August 1792, the day of the storming of the Tuileries by the Paris mob, who massacred the Swiss Guards. The French royal family subsequently fled through the gardens and sought sanctuary with the Legislative Assembly – but it was all in vain of course, for they all ended up losing their heads on the guillotine.

Misses Moberley and Jourdain obtained a plan of the gardens of the Petit Trianon, dated 1774, and were able to trace the route they had somehow taken as they temporarily walked out of the twentieth century and into eighteenth century. When they compared the map of the original gardens with that of the modern ones, there were significant discrepancies in the gardens' layout. In fact, according to the modern map, the route they had taken should have been impossible. Yet the old map made it quite clear that they had gone on a tour of the gardens as they had been laid out one hundred and twelve years before.

There are numerous examples of such local timeslips in my other *Haunted Liverpool* books, and the following strange tale details yet another of these excursions into another time, but the period in this case has never been determined.

Far above the burning streets of Toxteth on one July night in 1981, the eternal stars winked in the perfect silence of space. Carried downwind through the humid trees of Falkner Square by a zephyr, drifted CS gas mingled with the smoke from flaming upturned cars and a blazing Shell filling station. The distant stars of summer, meanwhile – Arcturus, Vega, Altair, Spica, Deneb and Regulus – glittered on regardless, and were captured in the eyepieces of a twelve-year-old boy's binoculars. His wide brown eyes beheld the spectacular night-time show in the heavens, as he stood in the backyard of his home on Harlow Street, oblivious to the Toxteth Riots which raged in the distance. After a while, Dennis decided to take a look at another part of the sky and so made the mistake of leaving the security of the backyard that night. A policeman noticed him carrying the binoculars and immediately assumed that he had stolen them. The black amateur astronomer tried to explain that they were his uncle's, and that he had been lent them to study the night sky, but the disbelieving policeman ignored his story and grabbed the binoculars and tried to take Dennis in for questioning.

Dennis managed to dodge the policeman and run away down an alleyway as the policeman swore after him. He kept on running, even after he had lost sight of the policeman. Dennis soon found himself caught up in the middle of the riot. Petrol bombs criss-crossed in front of him and police in riot gear were responding with force. Dennis was terrified. What had happened t his normally peaceful neighbourhood? He knew that he had to get back home, but each route he took landed him back amongst the crowds of angry rioters. His heart was racing but he kept his head and embarked upon a tortuous journey to get back to Harlow Street, but this time found his way blocked by looters being pursued by baton-wielding police. He decided to change tactics and made up his mind to try and reach his married sister's home in Aigburth instead, even though he wasn't too sure which street she lived in.

Dennis walked along disconsolately, heartbroken at the loss of his uncle's binoculars; it just wasn't fair, he would never get his hands on another pair and astronomy was his hobby. Thinking about the binoculars made him glance skywards and he stopped in his tracks as he watched a falling star trace a silvery path across the night sky. He became so distracted with his star-gazing, that he took a wrong turning, lost his bearings and ended up in the unfamiliar territory of the Dingle. He was well and truly lost.

As the ghostly ashen light of dawn filtered into the eastern sky, Dennis spotted a lonely out-of-place boy as young, and almost as lost-looking, as himself. The lad was pale-faced and bespectacled, with a red mop of untidy hair. He wore a black blazer and, incongruously, some blue pyjama bottoms. Dennis crossed the road to ask for directions to Aigburth Road but the bespectacled boy seemed to shrink back at his approach, as if he were afraid. He then scuttled up to the door of the nearest house, and in a well-spoken voice, nervously announced, "I live here".

Dennis instinctively knew that he was lying, and decided to challenge him. "Well go on then, knock if that's yer 'ouse. Bet yer won't."

"My dad's a policeman," replied the boy, with a tremor in his voice.

"No he ain't," said Dennis. "Stop telling lies. What're yer doing out at this time in the morning, anyway?"

"None of your business – I'm not lying, so there."

This was getting Dennis nowhere, so he just shook his head and walked on, upon which the boy suddenly blurted out, "Aigburth Road is in the other direction."

"Right, thanks, mate."

Dennis then told the boy what had happened; about the policeman taking his binoculars and the riots and the looting, and his not being able to get back home to Harlow Street. The boy, who eventually gave his name as Alex, had his own tale of woe to tell. He had run away from home because his mother and father were about to split up, and he had decided that he would rather "live off the land" than live with either one of them.

"Me dad left me mum ages ago, when I was a baby," said Dennis, in sympathy with his new companion.

Full of pity for his new friend, Alex offered him a Toffo. "That's really awful," he said. "Poor you."

The boys walked off into the beginning of a new day, and as Dennis chewed on the toffee, he remarked to Alex, "Yer speak dead posh, don't yer? Where're yer from?"

"Woolton," Alex replied rather huffily, annoyed at being labelled as 'posh'.

Dennis narrowed his eyes as he estimated how far his new companion must have walked, dressed like he was.

"Yer've come all the way from Woolton – in yer jimjams? Yer lucky yer 'aven't bin locked up, mate."

They both burst out laughing. Alex looked down at his legs; he hadn't noticed in his rush to get away that he was still wearing his pyjamas.

"Oh dear! I do look a bit stupid, don't I?"

He then told Dennis that he had planned to somehow find a ferry to Ireland, or the Isle of Man and then stow away on it. Dennis was intrigued by this plan, it was better than some of the adventure stories he read in his comics and his respect for his new friend grew, despite his pyjamas and his poshness. He and Alex took a short cut down a narrow alleyway and came upon a section of crumbling wall, through which they could see nothing but an expanse of green on the other side. They bent down and peered through a large crack in the bricks and beheld what seemed to be a vast forest which stretched as far as the eye could see. But that didn't make any sense; this was Liverpool, a big city, and the nearest forest was Delamere, which was miles away.

Alex and Dennis squeezed through the gaping crack in the back-alley wall and left behind the strife-torn city where the predawn air was filled with the odour of burning buildings from the riots. Through that crumbling graffiti-daubed wall they came upon another world, filled with the clean-air tranquillity of a mysterious and extensive forest. The young lads marvelled at how a forest as large as the one that sprawled ahead of them, could exist in the back-streets of Liverpool. It looked at least ten times bigger than Sefton Park! To the disbelieving mind of an adult, such a green spectacle was an impossibility, but the boys simply accepted and revelled in what they saw.

"This is called trespassing you know," announced prim-and-proper Alex, glancing back at the crack in the wall, but adventuresome Dennis waded on through the knee-high grass without a word of reply, and so they entered an enchanted forest, inhabited by a myriad singing and chattering birds. Anxiously, Alex followed, and the two boys soon lost sight of the wall with its jagged opening, as they moved deeper into the forest.

By the light of the rising sun in the middle of the forest and close to a tumbling stream, Dennis and Alex spotted a quaint thatched cottage with a wisp of smoke hanging in the air above its chimney. Alex was afraid and pleaded with his newfound friend not to call at the cottage.

"Let's get away from here, Dennis. I don't like it."

"Oh, don't be daft," laughed Dennis. "What're yer scared of? The bogey man?" and he cheekily peered through a bulging bull's eye window in the chocolate-box cottage and saw the distorted image of an old man in a chair squinting back at him. The man sprinted out of his chair and yanked open the front door.

"What do you two want?" he demanded, in some long forgotten Lancashire brogue.

Dennis thought fast: "Er, nothing! Er ... what time is it please, mate?"

"Time! Time!" snarled the old man. "I haven't got a clue what time it is, since I don't possess a clock. No timepiece is going to rule my life – daytime and night-time are the only times I recognise. I don't bother with any of that o'clock nonsense."

The oldster started to rant like a madman about the tyranny of time and about clocks, and how he'd like to smash them all, so Dennis and Alex quickly slipped away down a sloping gravel track that led to a majestic avenue of ancient trees. The avenue eventually brought the wandering boys into the grounds of a colossal Jacobean mansion that stood shrouded in mist in the distance. Dennis and Alex looked back to where they had come from, and were confronted with a baffling mystery – they could see no trace of their native Liverpool; not a single rooftop, nor a chimney, nor a church spire.

As the boys approached the mansion, they simultaneously became aware of the distant gallop of a horse's hooves – yet saw nothing – until, at last, Dennis detected a ghostly grey figure on horseback, emerging from the morning ground-mists, about four-hundred yards in the distance. Dennis stood there, fascinated, because the glorious early morning sunshine was reflecting off the rider as if he – well, as if he was wearing a suit of armour! Alex urged his friend to run back into the woods to hide, as he had a bad feeling about the approaching stranger, but within a minute the silvery rider was almost upon them. They hurried away whilst gazing up at the huge steed mounted by a figure clad from head to toe in knight's armour.

The horse pounded past the boys, then came to a sudden halt and turned to bar their way. The knight lifted the visor on his helmet, revealing an unexpected face – that of a stern but very attractive woman, in her forties perhaps. She reflexively placed her gauntlet on the hilt of her sheathed sword, and in loud but refined voice asked, "What are you doing on this land? Do you realise that you are trespassing?"

Alex dashed off in fright and as he did so a gunshot rang out and he fell to the ground.

Dennis swore out loud and bawled, "He's bin shot, you shot him!"

Fortunately, Alex picked himself up off the ground and told his Toxteth friend that he was fine; the bullet had whistled past his left ear and he'd dived to the grass reflexively.

"Think yourself lucky! Run off again and you'll be bagged!" warned the armour-clad woman. As if to underline her warning, she drew a long-bladed sword from its scabbard and pointed it threateningly at Dennis.

"Hey! You! Put that bloomin' thing away," shouted Dennis, audaciously. "Yer could kill somebody with that."

He and Alex then became aware of a boy around their own age, dressed in outlandish clothing, stepping out from behind a tree. In his right hand he held a smoking pistol and it was obviously he who taken the pot-shot at Alex. The boy was dressed in a Falu-red velvet jacket, pink satin waistcoat with frilly white lace trimmings, and a pair of black knee breeches. He wore his golden-blonde hair in lovelocks tied with blaze-orange ribbons.

"Mama!" he cried in an effeminate voice, "Are you alright? Who are these rascals?"

"We're not rascals," protested Dennis. "We're just two lost boys from Liverpool," and he clenched his fists ready to defend himself, when he saw the flamboyant long-haired boy with the pistol drawing near.

"Hayden!" snapped the female knight reaching down to her son. "Let me have that pistol right now!"

The boy reluctantly handed his eccentric mother the weapon and she trained it on the two trespassers and herded them towards the mansion, where the butler instructed them to sit at a long table in what turned out to be the dining hall. The head of the household subsequently identified herself as Lady Hathaway, when she entered the room a short time later, minus her suit of armour. She questioned Dennis and Alex about how they had come to trespass on her land, and when they described the crack in the wall, Lady Hathaway gave a slight nod. She seemed to know what they were talking about, for she became silent for a while with a far-away look in her eyes. This reverie ended with the aristocratic woman telling the boys: "You two will have to go back to whence you came. You are not allowed here."

Inquisitive Dennis wanted to know where exactly 'here' was, but Lady Hathaway was having none of it and remained tight-lipped. Picking her way through the forest, which she obviously knew like the back of her hand, she escorted the boys back to the crack in the wall and ordered them to go back through it. And so the lads squeezed through the opening into the dismal troubled world of 1981. When they looked back through the crack, there was no sign of any forest, nor of the aristocratic lady, just the grey backyard of an uninhabited house.

Alex had had his fill of adventure for the time being and gave up the romantic notion of going to sea. After showing Dennis which way to go, they both returned to their own homes. Dennis found that the police had been searching everywhere for him when he reached his house on Harlow Street, and his mother scolded him for staying out all night, before giving him a big hug. When Alex told his snooty squabbling parents about his new friend they were not impressed and he was forbidden to mix with the boy from Toxteth, as they didn't want him associating with children 'of that sort'.

Alex had other ideas, and he and Dennis would secretly meet up every weekend to go in search of that fabulous forest, and on many occasions they were indeed able to find it hidden in the brick backyard wall of an old alleyway, and they enjoyed many adventures, romances and intrigues with strange peoples in some uncharted land that is unrecorded on our dull maps. These adventures continued until 1985, when the bulldozer moved in and demolished the empty house with its idiosyncratic backyard wall. Both boys wept when they saw the pile of bricks and rubble; the tragic vestiges of the magical crack in the wall.

Dennis and Alex are now in their late thirties and are still the best of friends, and they swear that their adventures were not born out of childish imagination. I have interviewed the two men many times and I am convinced that they did share a genuine paranormal experience, which I am unable to explain. Maybe the crack in the wall was some kind of portal into a bygone age, and it is possible that that entry point may have now shifted to some other unlikely place. Perhaps the lost world of Dennis and Alex is still waiting to be rediscovered through some innocent-looking gap in a garden fence somewhere ...

SKEETCHY AND BUMPH

Lyons Street in Bootle was once the scene of so many murders, that it was renamed Beresford Street, in some vague attempt by the authorities to brush the notorious street's name under the carpet. The plan backfired, because after the name change, Lyons Street became known locally in the early twentieth century as the 'street that died of shame'. Street names have been changed before in an attempt to expunge their evil reputations; one only has to look at the changing of Leveson Street to Grenville Street in Victorian Liverpool, after of the shocking murder of a family that took place there in 1849 (see my *Wicked Liverpool*).

The notoriety which Lyons Street acquired can be traced back to a singularly heinous series of crimes – the brutal killings of several prostitutes by two sailors – which became known as the Teapot Murders, because Lyons was associated with the famous tea-brand during that period. If such infamy was not enough to blacken the street's name, two further terrible and widely-reported murders took place on Lyons Street: the vicious and cruel killing of Maggie Donoghue, who had her brains bashed out by fireman Jim McGuirk in 1903, and the mysterious and callous killing of six-year-old Tommy Foy, in 1908.

However, allow me to digress from the criminological history of that Bootle street, and accompany me, via your imagination, as I transport you back to Lyons Street in 1896, and specifically to a crumbling and draughty old terraced house at Number 48. The ground floor of this miserable building was one of those shops that sold everything, and was run by a Mrs Annie Burns.

In October 1896, Maureen Mack left Mackenzies' Boarding House in Howe Street, Bootle, after a heated argument with one of the other lodgers and set off to find somewhere else to live. She and her seven-year-old daughter Eileen found new lodgings over Annie Burns's shop on Lyons Street, and settled into their new home reasonably quickly. Mrs Mack slept in one room – a great luxury in those days – and little Eileen was given her very own room in the loft.

Late one October night, close to Halloween, a loud racket was heard to come from Eileen's room, and when her mother went to investigate, the girl was sitting up in bed looking very excited. She kept making vague and enigmatic remarks about two characters with whom she seemed to be familiar, and who went by the improbable names, Skeetchy and Bumph. When pressed for more details, Eileen said that they were two odd-looking shadows and that they had been visiting her over the past three nights.

"Oh, go back to sleep, Eileen!" said a grumpy and impatient Mrs Mack. "You're keeping the whole house awake. You'll get us thrown out if you're not careful, and you wouldn't like that, would you?" and she closed the bedroom door and went back to bed.

However, when Maureen Mack settled back into bed, she began to mull over the peculiar things that her daughter had told her. Eileen was neither a particularly bright, nor an overly imaginative child as a rule, and she was certainly not the sort to invent such an elaborate and bizarre story just to gain attention. So Mrs Mack accepted that there was a possibility that the girl was telling the truth and had genuinely seen something out of the ordinary – something supernatural perhaps.

On the following evening, Eileen went to bed at around 8 o'clock without any bother, and minutes later, Maureen, who had positioned herself at the foot of the attic stairs, heard strange-sounding voices coming from her daughter's room. She crept upstairs until she was right outside the loft door, then screwed up an eye, and peeped with the other one through the draughty keyhole. What Maureen saw caused her to tremble uncontrollably. A pair of sinister shadows, cast by two peculiar-looking but invisible beings, were moving about on the wall next to Eileen's bed. One of the figures was horned like the devil, but as bulky as an elephant, whilst the other was skinny, with pointed ears and a tapering cone-shaped head, and they were fighting one another.

Eileen, meanwhile, far from being frightened by all this, was sitting up in bed, chuckling and clapping her hands in glee at the antics of this Punch-and-Judy-style shadow play. Maureen Mack made the sign of the cross before bursting into the room to grab a startled Eileen from the clutches of the bizarre pair

"Mum! Put me down, they're my friends," cried Eileen, struggling to free herself from her mother's sturdy grip.

"Yes, leave her alone, you wench!" added the skinny silhouette, waving an angry fist at Maureen.

Maureen was having none of it. Screaming like a banshee, she ran down five flights of stairs in her nightdress, dragging a very disappointed Eileen after her.

Mother and daughter never returned to that house, much to Eileen's dismay. She missed her mysterious friends sorely, even though she didn't know what they were, or why they existed only as shadows. We will probably never know who Skeetchy and Bumph were either. There were – as far as I know – no further paranormal goings-on at Number 48 Lyons Street after that.

RED FACE

Beware if you happen to be travelling along Wavertree Road, be it during the night or in the daytime, for an old and particularly chilling apparition is often encountered along that stretch of tarmacadam.

The most recent sighting of the enigmatic 'Red Face' – which always manifests itself as a distorted crimson face, screwed up, as if in severe pain – was through the passenger window of a taxi travelling towards the Junction of Wavertree Road and Marmaduke and Overbury Streets, on the afternoon of Friday, 14 September 2007. The two passengers in the taxi stared in horror as the red luminous face of a man suddenly appeared in the right-hand window of the vehicle. The face appeared to be contorted and twisted in agony; its brow was deeply furrowed and its lips were moving as if it was desperately trying to speak but could not find its voice.

Ken Jones, one of the passengers who witnessed the frightening spectral face, clutched his twenty-year-old daughter's hand as she instinctively recoiled in horror. The disembodied face kept pace with the vehicle for about a hundred yards, shimmering with an eerie red glow in the taxi's right passenger window, before it vanished as the vehicle reached the traffic lights, leaving Ken Jones and his daughter looking at each other in shock and bewilderment.

This same red face has been seen many times before and seems to foretell tragedy. Many years ago I heard about the ghostly face being seen by numerous passengers in broad daylight, on board the Number 79 bus, as the vehicle travelled down Wavertree Road towards the junction at Durning Road, Tunnel Road and Picton Road. The face seemed to be crying on that occasion, as it hovered on the corner of Durning Road. The next day a car crashed at that exact same spot and several people died.

The earliest reported sighting of the disembodied face was in 1973, when a woman driving to Crawfords mini-market on Wavertree Road, came across it one rainy afternoon, as she passed the corner of Dorothy Street. On that occasion the face was only seen in the right-hand wing mirror of the woman's mini for just a fleeting moment – but it was enough! On the following day, the same driver crashed at that exact spot, but fortunately, on this occasion, there were no serious consequences and she only sustained minor injuries.

Just whose ghost the red face represents has never been established, although one medium has told me that she thinks it is the earthbound spirit of a police motorcyclist, who died on Wavertree Road after crashing into a van in the 1970s.

THE KNOTTY ASH CANNIBALS

At around 7 o'clock on the Saturday night of 26 August 1893, a likeable forty-year-old local man, John Cargill, was enjoying his pint of bitter at the Childwall Abbey Hotel, whilst eavesdropping on the conversation which the landlady, Miss Rimmer, was having with a group of five distinguished-looking strangers. The group was made up of five balding businessmen, all in their fifties, and each exhibited the professional confidence of say a bank manager, a doctor, or an architect, perhaps. They each politely declined Miss Rimmer's invitation to sample the pub's famous Irish stew, cooked freshly that day by the chef, Mulligan. In fact, the five men refused all offers of food, saying they wanted to keep a hearty appetite for a great banquet due to be held at their friend's home in about an hour's time.

Apparently, their host was a rich local man by the name of Horton, and that word 'rich' instantly made Cargill's ears prick up, because, unknown to the rest of Childwall's community, he was an audacious burglar, wanted by the police across the whole of Lancashire. By day, Cargill loafed about in the bar of the Childwall Abbey Hotel, or did odd-jobs as the local handyman of the neighbourhood. Ironically, when Childwall vicarage had been burgled by an unscrupulous youth some weeks before, Cargill had apprehended the culprit and the Reverend Winter had paid him a small reward, unaware that he was himself a house-breaker of great skill and cunning.

To get back to the story ... upon this pleasantly warm August Saturday night, Cargill overheard several of the five men boasting about the fabulous wealth of their host-to-be, and one even let slip his address: 46 Thomas Lane, Knotty Ash. Cargill was well aware that the best time to burgle a house was during the aftermath of a party, when, with a bit of luck, the host would be out cold with a bellyful of drink and food. So the information he had gleaned from the businessmen was doubly useful, and he was already busy formulating a plan to relieve his unfortunate victim of some of his fabled wealth.

Long after midnight, when all the guests had left the party in Knotty Ash and the house was in darkness, Cargill unfolded his nifty telescopic ladder and gained entry into what turned out to be the dining room of the impressive detached house. As he slid silently through the window, he shone his bull's eye lantern across the long table and saw ashtrays overflowing with cigar and cigarette butts and the remains of an array of sumptuous dishes laid out on silver plates, and several opened bottles containing various quantities of red wine.

Cargill greedily took a mighty swig from one of these bottles to sample what he imagined to be a delightful top quality Beaujolais – and instead he froze in shock when he realised that the bottle contained something glutinous and vile, with a vaguely familiar taste – that of blood! Retching, Cargill spat out the sticky crimson goo and looked at the bottle's label; there was an unknown word (possibly a Latin one) in italicised writing upon it. He felt ill at ease all of a sudden and shone his torch over the plates once more and this time noticed a skull lying on one of the silver platters. The skull was no plastic mock-up, or even part of a medical student's skeleton. No – this skull was still fresh and still had strips of flesh and torn muscle hanging from it. It was obviously meant to be part of the feast – probably the centre-piece – because it was ringed with bunches of grapes and leaves, and small cutlets of something, which decency forbids me to mention, that made the burglar's flesh creep.

As Cargill shone his torch further down the table it illuminated the remains of the ribs of this human victim. There could be no doubt about it, Cargill had stumbled into the aftermath of what he now recognised as a cannibal feast. The ribs were scattered about the dish, having been stripped bare of most of their flesh and they glistened white in the light from the torch. Cargill had been a villain all his adult life, but this was beyond villainy. It was depraved and debauched and he wanted absolutely nothing to do with it. Abandoning all his get-rich-quick plans, he made his way back to the open window and almost fell to the ground down his telescopic ladder.

So incensed was he about the sick spectacle that he had happened upon, that the next day he wrote an anonymous 'angry of Childwall' letter to the police, tipping them off about the disgusting cannibals' banquet. However, Cargill's correspondence was apparently not taken seriously, because on the following Saturday, the five strangers turned up once again at the Childwall Abbey Hotel and played bowls and quoits in the pub gardens, as bold as brass.

Cargill was caught red-handed burgling another house a year later and whilst awaiting trial, he told the police about the Knotty Ash cannibal, Horton. The accusation was investigated, but they found his home on Thomas Lane occupied by a quiet accountant by the name of Hilditch and could find no evidence of any cannibalistic activities.

We may discover more about this intriguing, though sickening case one day, but what I do know is that Number 46 Thomas Lane used to be haunted by a wailing woman dressed in a long white gown – possibly a burial shroud – in Edwardian times. The unidentified ghost was seen in 1901 – when Number 46 was an infant's school – by no less a person than the school's headmistress, Miss Margaret Rogers. Miss Rogers allegedly saw the partially transparent phantom after school hours, along with one of the cleaners, as it glided straight through the classroom chalkboard. The apparition was seen again thereafter by a cleaner named Crawford, who noticed the bare feet of the ghost protruding from beneath its pale garment, as she scrubbed the hallway tiles on her knees. She looked up, and seeing the ghastly face of the supernatural visitor peering from beneath a hood, almost passed out. The ghost then vanished.

For a while there was a rumour that the woman in white was the ghost of a woman who had been murdered and buried under the foundations of Number 46, but then the sightings became less frequent, the spectre retired and haunted no more. Could there be any connection between this ghost and the cannibal feast which Cargill reported? Like so many of these supernatural mysteries, all we can do is wait and see if more will be revealed in time.

THE SPEKE HALL WEREWOLF

One of the finest Elizabethan manor houses in the country is our own Speke Hall, and in its present form it dates back to a period that runs from 1490 to 1612, although there was a building that stood on the site of today's Grade I listed building, many years before that. Not many Liverpudlians are aware that there exists an exact – but earthquake-proof – replica of Speke Hall, built in 1912, by the millionaire Percy Morgan, in California, but, of course, our beautifully preserved original building is the genuine article and is one of the top tourist attractions of the region.

I have visited the historic manor house in Speke many times on ghost-vigils, and also to deliver talks on the supernatural, and I am well-acquainted with all of the spooky tales associated with the Hall, as well as the paranormal goings-on within its grounds. I am aware of the hackneyed and inaccurate story about the White Lady – thought to be the ghost of Mary Norris – who allegedly haunts the Tapestry Room, and I am also very familiar with the authentic tale of the smirking cavalier, who haunts a loft at the Hall, but few ghost-hunters have heard about the werewolf, which is said to roam the grounds of the half-timbered manor house.

I have received many reports of this terrifying creature over the years, and some believe it came into existence around the time of Thomas Norris, who inherited the manor of Speke, in 1467. A woman in her eighties by the name of Nerys told me back in the 1970s that the werewolf roamed the woods that lay adjacent to the lonely lane known as 'The Walk', which runs from Speke Hall to the avenue that bears its name. Her account, taken on its own would have amounted to nothing but hearsay, but many times over the years I have received recurring reports of a strange-looking wolf-like animal being at large in the area around Speke Hall. According to Nerys, who was of Romany descent, her father told her that in the fifteenth century, an aristocratic Lancashire rake called Lathom, raped a gypsy girl on the estate. The girl's grandmother issued a powerful curse on whoever was responsible for the terrible deed, proclaiming that the depraved guilty person would become as low as an animal of the forest, as a punishment for behaving like a degenerate beast.

The gypsies eventually moved on, leaving the locals of Speke wondering if the old Romany woman's curse would come to pass. Not long afterwards, on the night of a full moon, the despicable nobleman Lathom was in the woods trying to seduce another young woman, this time a relative of the Norris family, who, at that time, owned Speke Hall. The lewd Lathom had only one thought in his mind, and that was to have sex with the young lady. However, being from an upright Catholic family, she made it plain that kissing was as far as she was prepared to go; she would not consent to having sexual intercourse with him. But Lathom was not to be deflected from his evil intentions, and his handsome face became contorted with frustrated rage when she denied him. He gritted his teeth and began to snarl in the most disturbing way, and the object of his desire, despite feeling weak in the legs from fear, ran off, terrified. She glanced around a few moments later and saw Lathom running after her – down on all fours – like an animal! This sight only served to increase the girl's terror, and she began to scream hysterically as she rushed blindly on into the depths of the woods.

Just when the young lady was about to pass out from the distress of her ordeal, she came upon a clearing in the woods where, to her enormous relief, three poachers were sitting hunched around a small fire. She stumbled and fell on to one of these men, but being out of breath, she was unable to warn them of the unspeakable horror that was heading their way. Before she could regain her composure, Lathom suddenly burst out of the undergrowth, transformed by now into a massive, slavering werewolf, yet still decked out in the vestiges of a ragged white shirt and trousers, which his bulging muscles had burst open at the seams.

One of the poachers leapt to his feet and lit a torch from the flames of the fire and swung it wildly at the monstrous creature, in an attempt to keep it at bay, but the beast reared up and stood on its hind legs, as only a werewolf can, then lunged forward to tear the poacher's torch-wielding forearm apart. The two other poachers put up a valiant but futile fight with the werewolf, as the girl ran for her life back to Speke Hall. Legend has it that Lathom killed all three poachers and returned home later that night naked, bloodied and barefoot to his home in Garston.

Lathom's father disowned his accursed son and threw him out of the house to fend for himself. This rejection, coupled with the knowledge of what he had become and what he had done to the three poachers, caused Lathom to commit suicide, but for some reason his earthbound spirit keeps returning in the shape-shifted form of a werewolf.

So much for the folklore, but let us now come forward to 1973, for in the winter of that year, a group of Territorial Army soldiers were camping in Stockton's Wood, overlooking Speke Hall and the perimeter of what was then known as Speke Airport. The time was around four o'clock and already dusk was falling. The soldiers were clustered around a small fire trying to keep warm, and one of them, a man in his thirties named Terry, was attempting to cook sausages over the flames in a small frying pan, when suddenly, an unearthly howl reverberated through the woods. It was nothing like the howl of a domestic dog, they all agreed, and more like that of a wolf.

One of the group then beheld a frightening sight. To the left of Stockton's Wood there was a farm – possibly Speke Home Farm, which is situated quite close to the airport – and walking towards this farm with a loping gait, was an unusually large and somewhat elongated wolf, grey in colour. The soldier who spotted this strange creature alerted his colleagues, and they all watched as the bizarre-looking animal circled the farm for several minutes. Then it was startled by the approach of a vehicle driven by a visitor to the farm, and it turned away and bounded off into Stockton's Wood.

As this was taking place, snow had begun to fall, and within minutes, a knife-edged wind from the river had got up, and a full-blown blizzard ensued. The soldiers' orders were to camp out until 7pm, but they made a joint decision, with the agreement of the sergeant, to leave the woods early, not just on account of the inclement weather, but also because of the strange 'wolf' they had just been watching. After gobbling down the half-cooked sausages, the soldiers packed up their kit and headed towards the long tree-lined avenue leading from Speke Hall. As they neared the road, they encountered the wolf for the second time that day. It was standing on its enormous hind legs, leaning casually against a

28

tree, and was evidently at least six feet in height – possibly more.

The sergeant in charge of the volunteer soldiers, whispered a hasty command for his troops to keep absolutely still and silent, as he feared the unidentified but fearsome animal might attack at any moment. The last wolves in Britain became extinct around 1680, although there have been alleged encounters with animals that are possibly surviving wolves. Even if the terrifying creature standing on its hind legs was one of these survivors, it still did not look like a normal wolf. Its body was thickset at the front and tapered towards the hind legs, and its face seemed almost human, with the same type of lively eyes seen in an intelligent specimen of chimpanzee or ape. The real giveaway was the absence of a tail, one of the well-documented features of a genuine werewolf. The soldiers carried no weapons, and they waited with bated breath, expecting the creature to attack at any moment, but it merely bared its teeth and snarled at them, before dropping down on to all fours and sloping off down the lane – towards Speke Hall.

The incident had unsettled the soldiers, including the sergeant, who made enquiries with the staff at the Hall as to the nature of beast, and why it was allowed to roam freely in an area where there were people about. However, he was wasting his time, because no one was prepared to take his account of the wolf encounter seriously.

In the autumn of that year, what was undoubtedly the same creature was seen once more, this time by a couple of teenagers, Tony and Judy. They had been seeing each other for just a fortnight, and had rendezvoused at a secluded spot near the Dunlop Factory, when Tony saw something that looked like an over-sized Great Dane bounding past him towards Stockton's Wood. Judy thought he was joking at first, and she pulled him towards her and they started to kiss, until they were both startled by a deep-throated growl from somewhere close by. Judy let out a scream as she caught sight of the beast over Tony's shoulder. As he turned to see what it was, something too fast for his eyes to follow, charged at them both, knocking Judy backwards by six feet. She lay stunned in the grass, and Tony stood there for a second in shock. He watched with relief as the strange animal raced away from, but then its path ominously began to curve and slow. The unearthly-looking animal turned around and made another charge at the couple.

Tony ran to Judy's aid and crouched down to help her up. In total horror and disbelief he realised that the 'hound' with the red glinting eyes, must, in fact, be a species of huge wolf. It had run about a hundred yards away but it was now hurtling back towards them, baring its fanged teeth. In a pathetically lame attempt to defend himself and his girlfriend, Tony raised his fist as the wolf was about to pounce, and almost simultaneously, an ear-splitting explosion blasted through the air. The overgrown wolf stopped in its tracks abandoning its charge and then running off towards the woods.

Tony looked around to see where the explosion had come from. To his right stood a man wearing a deerstalker hat, tweed jacket, green canvas trousers and Wellington boots – and he was wielding a smoking shotgun. Around his neck there was a strap that held a cased SLR camera, and around his waist, a British Army webbing belt, with a holster and various other pieces of equipment attached to it.

In a well-spoken voice, the armed stranger said, "I strongly advise you to get out of this area right now."

"What the hell was that thing?" asked Judy, struggling to her feet and hanging on to her boyfriend for dear life.

By way of reply, the stranger pointed towards a path and told them to leave immediately that way, and he then proceeded towards the woods.

Tony shouted after him: "Was that a wolf? Hey! You! I'm asking you, was that a wolf?"

Their saviour made no reply, but just kept on walking towards the woods, obviously tracking his quarry. Tony and Judy ran from that field without so much as a backward glance and they never went near that area again. The identity of the man with the shotgun remains a mystery.

I mentioned this case on the radio a few years ago and asked the man in question to get in touch, but he never did, although a few listeners who thought they had seen him called in. A university lecturer said he believed the man was a cryptozoologist – a person who hunts for animals that are either supposed to be extinct, or unknown to zoologists.

The Surrey Puma is an excellent example of a creature sought by the cryptozoologist. The puma has been spotted at various locations around the Surrey countryside since the 1960s, although there is a very early record of a large cat-like animal in a tree near Waverley Abbey, a mile south of Farnham in Surrey, in 1770. The Surrey Puma has been seen by a succession of credible witnesses over the years, and has been hunted by a Canadian tracker, soldiers, and policemen, and was even shot at several times, apparently without any effect – the puma simply ran off, and was later seen to be unharmed.

In 1966, big-game hunters arrived in the wilds of Surrey to go 'on safari' – but all to no avail – because the big cat was always one step ahead of its determined pursuers. In 1968, a rumour circulated that the puma had been shot dead by a farmer, but in the following year the mysterious puma was seen again, apparently in the best of health. Sceptics who doubt the existence of a big cat in Surrey have argued that such a beast would need to eat regular and substantial quantities of fresh meat in order to survive, yet it doesn't seem to kill anything. They missed the fact that there are over six thousand violent attacks on farm animals each year, and although a large percentage of these attacks are probably the work of dogs, there is a significant percentage that can never be satisfactorily explained.

Situated in the Weald, the Surrey village of Cranleigh has been the scene of many mysterious attacks by wolf-like creatures over the years. Full-grown deer have been torn apart by an unidentified predator resembling an enormous wolf, which suspiciously goes to ground very quickly, apparently into the village. In *Haunted Liverpool 3* I told the story of the Welsh Werewolf, and how it killed people, and in later years killed and ate whole lambs, leaving the spines intact. In one case, a 250-pound prize ram was ripped to shreds by one of these mysterious predators.

In 1989 an unidentified beast that may have been the Speke Werewolf was spotted prowling along Banks Lane, close to the Speke Dams. The witness, Mike Allen, was a motorist from Walton who had lost his bearings at the Speke Hall Avenue roundabout, after a visit to a relative near Mill Wood. Mr Allen was reversing along a secluded stretch of Banks Lane at around 9.30pm, when he caught a huge grey wolf-like animal in his headlights. The creature had a loping gait, and Mr Allen noticed that it had no tail – not even the stub of a tail like a Manx cat – and was like something out of a horror movie.

The animal slowly turned to face the car and its eyes reflected back a steady green light, which, coupled with the its fearsome face, inspired terror in Mike Allen. He stalled the car, restarted it in a cold sweat, then drove off at high speed down the lane, back towards the roundabout. When he looked in his rear view mirror, he realised that the wolf was chasing his vehicle. He was so terrified that he drove straight through the give-way markings at the roundabout and almost collided with another car. By the time he reached Speke Road, he saw, to his relief, that the horrific animal had given up the chase.

There have been hundreds of big cat sightings in this country, and no one is quite sure exactly what these animals are, or where they have come from. Are they the descendants of illegally released circus animals, or imported lions, pumas and cougars. Perhaps their owners could no longer afford their upkeep, or could no longer handle them? There may be a few rational explanations for some of these sightings, but the Werewolf of Speke Hall remains an unsettling puzzler.

A Tune to Conjure With

A great percentage of the sorcery practised by the magicians of old was in the form of spoken magic and chants and incantations. Moses was said to have recited an esoteric phrase containing the word Shemhamforash – an epithet for the seventy-two-letter name of God – when he stretched out his hand to part the Red Sea. Magicians nowadays occasionally use the word Abracadabra as part of their act, but in ancient times this word was an incantation that was taken very seriously, as it was based on the Aramaic words Avra Kedabra, which mean, "I create as I speak", and it is a reference to God creating the Universe by speaking ("Let there be light").

Singing is another way of effecting spells, and today's hymns are the vestiges of the days gone by when men and women regularly chanted incantations to higher beings.

In the 1960s, in Liverpool, there was an alleged case of a group of young men who inadvertently chanted an ancient spell and so accidentally conjured up a host of terrifying demons. This took place in 1965, at the same time as the Beatles were steadily conquering the world through their music. A group of four musicians in their twenties, calling themselves Children of the Night, were struggling to make it big, but frequently lamented that their song-writing skills were abysmal and were letting them down.

One evening, after a disastrous performance at a club, in which they had been booed by the audience, they were drowning their sorrows at the Carnarvon Castle public house in Tarleton Street, where Christopher, the lead singer of the group, suddenly had a quirky idea. Taking a crumpled piece of paper from his pocket, he tore it into twelve squares, and upon these scraps he wrote the letters of the seven natural musical notes – C D E F G A B – and on each of the five other squares he scribbled down the flat notes. Christopher then upturned his empty drinking glass and persuaded the other members of the group to put their index fingers upon it.

The four men sat in the corner of the pub, watched by an audience of bemused drinkers, as they conducted an ad hoc Ouija session.

Christopher wrote down the notes towards which the glass slid, and that evening he and a fellow 'Child of the Night', went back to a flat overlooking Sefton Park and attempted to play the Ouija composition on a harpsichord. The glass had composed a piece that began with the notes E B C and D, played in a recurring sequence, before a more complex tune commenced. The result was a psychaedelic melody, which caused all Hell to break loose in that flat – quite literally. The harpsichord vibrated violently, and a mirror on the wall loudly cracked in two. Doors and windows flew open and there were thuds on the walls; and then came the unearthly sound of moaning voices talking in unknown languages.

Jason was so disturbed by the weird turn of events, that he shouted to Christopher to stop playing the eerie tune, but his friend was like a man possessed, and was staring at the keyboard with bulging eyes as his fingers rippled along the keys at breakneck speed. Jason had seen enough. He dashed out of the flat without even picking up his coat. Unfortunately, he made the mistake of fleeing to his home in Aigburth Vale via Sefton Park. He was well into the dark and deserted park before he realised that something grotesque, surreal and truly terrifying was galumphing after him. A backward glance revealed a hideous creature with beady ruby-red eyes, spindly arms and legs and a long pointed snout. This demonic monstrosity, accidentally conjured up by the Ouija music, was no trick of the imagination, because it was also seen by a courting couple in the park, as well as the landlady of Jason's flat.

Throughout that long and terrible night, Jason slept with his late mother's rosary beads entwined around his neck and now and then he would open his eyes and see the silhouette of the 'thing' that had chased him across the park, still scratching at his bedroom window. But this was not the worst of it – far from it.

On the following morning, Jason went back to the flat to check on his friend, only to find that his fellow band member Christopher had been found dead – of 'natural causes' – on the floor of his flat. He had been discovered lying in a weird and unnatural posture. Instinctively realising what had caused his friend's death, Jason snatched the scribbled musical notes from Christopher's flat and took them back to his. He still has them in his possession to this day, but he has not yet summoned up the courage to play those notes again, terrified of what he might unleash were he to do so.

I have studied ancient chants and invocation music for many years, and on several occasions I have been intrigued to spot tunes within popular musical hits that contain notes very close to melodies that have been used by occultists to conjure up all sorts of demons and other supernatural entities. The opening guitar riff of the Detroit Spinners' old hit 'It's a Shame' – written in partnership with Stevie Wonder – is very close to a mystical melody that was once played to conjure up spirits in medieval times. Marc Bolan's songs also contain rhythms and melodies that have a striking similarity to occult chants and beats, and Bolan himself admitted that many of his songs had paranormal origins.

The Great God Pan was also the god of music – and Pan has always been classed as an important figure in occult lore, being worshipped today by Wiccans and Pagans alike. He is unusual because he was regarded as the only god who was dead. According to the Greek historian Plutarch, in the reign of the Roman Emperor Tiberius (42 BC-37 AD), the news of Pan's death came to a sailor named Thamus, who was on his way to Italy via the island of Paxi, when a divine spectral voice called to him across the waters, saying, "Thamus, are you there? When you reach Palodes, take care to proclaim that the great god Pan is dead." Thamus did this, and the strange news was received by the people who heard it with loud wails and much lamenting.

When Rock and Roll first appeared on the music scene in the 1950s, it was literally branded as 'the Devil's music' by the establishment, as nothing like it had been heard before, and it captured the imagination of a whole new generation of young people and, at times, seemed to take them over.

Anxiety about the supernatural side of music dates back to before the Rock and Roll era. In the 1930s a song called 'Gloomy Sunday' (see

Haunted Liverpool 3) was banned by the BBC, as it allegedly caused a spate of suicides because it sounded so mournful. Another song that even musicians consider to be very unlucky, is entitled 'I Dreamt I Dwelt in Marble Halls' from a musical called *The Bohemian Girl*. Even to hum the tune is said to invite bad luck and news of a death.

In the 1930s, a rumour travelled the world which claimed that blues legend Robert Johnston had obtained his musical skills after making a pact with the Devil at a deserted country crossroads. The very same rumour was later repeated in the 1970s, this time alleging that Jimi Hendrix had entered into a pact with Satan in exchange for his phenomenal guitar talent.

In the late 1960s, Christian fundamentalist preachers accused record companies of being fronts for Satanic organisations, which were hiding secret subliminal messages in the records. Of course, many bands thought that these accusations were a good publicity gimmick, and some, like Black Sabbath and Led Zeppelin, revelled in all the paranoia. There was even a rumour that Led Zeppelin's Jimmy Page was a black magician, although it is true that Page once bought and lived in a huge mansion on the banks of Loch Ness that was owned by the prominent Devil worshipper Aleister Crowley.

Around this time, the Beatles released their landmark *Sergeant Pepper's Lonely Hearts Club Band* album, which contained many mysterious tracks which have never been satisfactorily explained. Some fans say there is the sound of a car crash being played in reverse in 'Being for the Benefit of Mr Kite', and the allegedly rude message that is played backwards at the end of the album was once thought to be a message from the Devil himself. The album's producer George Martin has always vehemently maintained that the end-track contains nothing sinister at all; merely a random collection of spliced tapes of sounds and conversations. The fans of the Beatles thought otherwise, and made much of the fact of Satan-worshipper Aleister Crowley being included in the famous crowd scene on the album cover of *Sergeant Pepper*.

When the Beatles released their widely acclaimed *White Album*, a year later, Charles Manson claimed that one of their songs, 'Helter Skelter', had driven him and his band of followers to embark on a killing spree which culminated in the grotesque murder of the heavily-pregnant actress Sharon Tate. Manson also claimed that another Beatles song, 'Blackbird', contained disguised messages about a future race war. He maintained that one of the lyrics in the song: 'Take these broken wings and learn to fly' was actually referring to a future time when the black citizens of America would rise up and revolt against their white oppressors.

By the late 1980s and early 1990s, the heavy metal music scene had become another source of bizarre rumours. There were stories in the world-wide media about youths being driven to 'heavy-metal suicide' after listening to certain tracks on heavy metal albums. The tracks were said to contain suicidal instructions to the listener, that had been 'back-masked', or played backwards, just below the audible level.

In 1990, the families of two dead youths sought damages of over three million dollars from heavy metal band Judas Priest and CBS records, claiming that their two teenaged sons had shot themselves after being inspired by the band's evil-sounding music.

THROUGH THE TIME BARRIER

I have covered the subject of timewarps several times before in my books and columns in the newspapers, and they never cease to fascinate me, because they force us to look at the world in a different light. We tend to think of 'yesterday' as something that is dead and gone forever, and the future as something that does not yet exist, whereas in actual fact, yesterday, although out of sight, and apparently unreachable, still exists back in the past along the time dimension, and the future already exists as a real 'place' along the same dimension in another direction – even though common sense and our everyday experience tells us otherwise. What follows is an incredible timeslip incident that was reported to me just recently.

In 2006, nineteen-year-old Sean – a drug user and petty criminal known to the police – was out shoplifting, to finance his habit, in

Liverpool city centre, when he was spotted and chased by a security guard down Hanover Street. He took a sharp turn and then dashed down a dead-end street known as Brooks Alley, and it was there that he began to feel a sensation of tightness across his chest. He immediately recognised the symptoms of a mild asthma attack and quickly took out his inhaler, shook it, and breathed in the medication from it. Sean kept one eye on the corner of the alley, as he expected the guard to come running round it at any minute, but he never did. It was at this point that he realised that something odd had taken place.

After a few minutes, the inhaler had taken effect and his breathing had returned to normal, yet something was still amiss but he couldn't quite put his finger on it. When he was sure that the coast was clear, he strolled out into a Hanover Street, trying to look as casual as he could. The street seemed unaccountably different. The road surface and pavements looked unfamiliar, and the vehicles trundling past him were like nothing Sean had ever seen before. The roadworks and cranes of the 'Big Dig' were nowhere to be seen, and the people walking by were dressed bizarrely. He noticed that it was now overcast and raining – whereas it had been bright and sunny only moments before. Two young men walked past Sean wearing anoraks which bore no brand-names, or manufacturer's logos, which struck him as odd, since virtually everything these days had such labels; whether somebody was wearing the right designer labels, was the way Sean and his mates decided whether somebody was 'cool' or not.

Sean then wandered towards Bold Street and noticed that there were traffic lights and access at the bottom of the street, where it should have been pedestrianised and, just as puzzling, there were bushes next to the Lyceum, where a drinking establishment was usually located. Suddenly feeling like a stranger in his own city, he pulled up his hood and mingled with the oddly-dressed shoppers and city workers. Every location he visited looked unreal, and gradually, the youth realised that he had somehow travelled back into the past, but he could not be sure which year it was, or even which decade, and he became very anxious and disorientated.

He instinctively reached for the security of his mobile phone but found that he could not get a signal, no matter where he went to in town. He suddenly had an idea and walked to a newspaper kiosk on Ranelagh Street, next to Central Station, and took a look at the date on the front page of the *Daily Post*. It was Thursday, 18 May 1967. Far from allaying his fears, this revelation brought on an anxiety attack and Sean ran back to Brooks Alley, the place where it had all started to go wrong. He kept glancing at his mobile, hoping for some reassuring communication from his mates, but the message on its screen stayed the same – no network available.

Suddenly, the alleyway seemed claustrophobic; he was confused and began to swear to himself, as panic tightened its grip on him. He felt as if he was going insane, and just wanted to return to his own time and to the few friends he had in 2006. His parents had long disowned him, but he cherished the three good companions who now formed his surrogate family. Trying to control the rising panic which was making him feel breathless again, he hurried up the road towards the Adelphi Hotel, stopping near a branch of H Samuel, the jewellers. Here at last he was relieved to find that he a signal on his mobile phone. The buildings and people in the immediate vicinity took on their familiar forms again all of a sudden, yet when he looked down to the other end of Ranelagh Street, he could see that the people there were still dressed in the styles of 1967.

Sean had no intention of standing around trying to unravel this paradox, and instead hurried off towards Brownlow Hill to catch the bus home. I have interviewed Sean on four separate occasions, and he has not changed one detail of his story. The security guard who chased him down Brooks Alley remembers Sean only too well and described to me how he had literally seemed to vanish into thin air down that cul-de-sac. Sean's three close friends added their weight to the authenticity of the account and confirmed that he was badly shaken-up by his experience. I have also carefully investigated the full and detailed descriptions of Liverpool city centre, which Sean gave to me about his alleged accidental trip into the past and I discovered them to be accurate in every respect for the date on which he saw on the copies of the *Daily Post*.

There have been many timeslip incidents reported in that particular area near Bold Street, and I believe there is actually a 'crack', or some faultline or weakness in time in the vicinity. In *Haunted Liverpool 2*, I reported a very interesting timewarp in which an off-duty policeman and a young female shopper found themselves in the Bold Street of the 1950s.

Why are there so many timeslip incidents in this area of Liverpool? Some investigators attribute them to the high-voltage lines feeding Central Station, coupled with the fact that there is a quartz component in the sandstone bedrock below the streets of Liverpool, which might somehow be responsible for these localised timeslips through an effect known as piezoelectricity. Perhaps some oscillation of the quartz is generating electrical fields around the Bold Street area, but I admit, that it is an insubstantial and unsubstantiated theory at the moment.

Other forces may be at work in the area, including geomagnetism. In June 2007, I was contacted (by snail mail) by a Mr Stewart, who wrote to warn me about getting 'amateurs' interested in the Bold Street timewarps through my articles in the papers. He told me how, in 1978, after studying several timeslip incidents in Bold Street reported to him via family members and friends, he had decided to try and induce a timewarp himself, using powerful electrical equipment. Mr Stewart employed a bank of car batteries stockpiled in the back of a van to power a circuit which energised Tesla coils arranged in the shape of a five-sided pentagon. The hazardous experiment resulted in Mr Stewart being blasted by an electrical bolt, which burnt a hole in his chest and almost killed him. Not long afterwards, a horse-drawn cab was seen on Hanover Street, close to where Mr Stewart had carried out his almost lethal experiment. The 'ghost' of the horse-drawn cab has also been reported to me in this century, and may have more to do with the dimensions of time than the supernatural (or are the two interchangeable terms?)

In early 2007, I received over thirty reports from people who had experienced various forms of 'time-slippage' in an area bounded by Bold Street, Hardman Street, Hope Street, and Mount Pleasant. I also received a few equally intriguing reports of timeslips on Church Street, but more of those later. Here is the first of these timeslip accounts.

* * *

In the winter of 1977, Roger, a man in his twenties, climbed into his car on Bold Place (behind St Luke's Church, Hardman Street) and set off for the Len Crawford Car Care Centre on Long Lane, Aintree, as his vehicle was due for its MOT test. The plan was for Roger to leave his Ford

41

Cortina at the Car Care Centre, while he waited in his mother's Aintree home. However, something unimaginable and incredible happened to Roger that wintry morning. He drove up Hardman Street, and slowed as he approached the traffic lights. As he did so he momentarily glanced to the left, into the window of an electrical goods store, then looked back through his windscreen at the road ahead. The lights had changed to green and so Roger swung left into Hope Street – and found himself on course for a head-on collision with a massive green tram which was rattling on its tracks towards him. Roger had not seen such a tram since he was a child, and he knew they had been discontinued some time in the late 1950s.

Roger braced himself for the collision, and the tram rammed the Cortina head-on, and then passed straight through it! Roger felt a cold rushing sensation coursing through his body as the ethereal tram passed straight through both himself and the car. He was in shock for a few minutes, and he sat in his car outside the Philharmonic pub, trying to fathom exactly what had just taken place. He finally felt able to get out of his car and he inspected the vehicle's bodywork to see if the Cortina had sustained any damage, but not a scratch could he find.

As he was inspecting his car and beginning to doubt his own sanity, sixty-year-old Mona Johnson came up to him and said that she had witnessed the phantom tram passing through the Cortina. What a relief! Here was proof that he had not imagined it. Mona told him that as the green tram swerved through the car and into Hardman Street, she had seen the road surface change from smooth tarmac to a cobblestones. Seconds later, the green tram faded away, along with the clattering sound it had made. To this day, Roger is still baffled by the timeslip incident and does not know what to make of it.

* * *

However, not all timeslips reveal the past; some also reveal the future. In 2002, a woman working at Littlewoods on Church Street told me of several timewarp incidents, which apparently showed her the way the department store would look in the future. The woman concerned was returning from her lunch break, and was travelling up the escalator to the floor on which she worked, when she took 'a funny turn'. She staggered off the escalator feeling light-headed, and instead of seeing the floor as it normally was, she saw an unfamiliar store with strange garments on display and futuristic light-fittings set into the ceiling. Some of the garments were priced very low – one, two and three pounds – and this puzzled the already confused member of staff, because she knew the price of everything in her department on that floor and nothing was as cheap as the items of clothing she could see hanging up in the strangely altered store. Stranger still, there wasn't a soul about, so she went back downstairs to alert another member of staff to the bizarre goings-on upstairs.

When the two women went back up the escalator they found the floor looking perfectly normal, with all the usual light-fittings and familiar layouts. Nothing was now amiss and everything bore the price tags they usually bore.

Years later, of course, the Littlewoods flagship store on Church Street closed its doors for the last time and the discount store Primark took over the building and totally refurbished it. The former employee of Littlewoods who had experienced the 'funny turn' decided to visit the new Primark store on Church Street, just out of curiosity – and she was stunned to discover that she had already glimpsed the layout of the upper floor of the store that day back in 2002. The same ultra-modern light-fittings were set in the ceiling, and the low-price garments she had seen five years before were all there. The woman was at a loss to explain just how this had happened, but it seems it was one of those rare timeslip incidents where the future is briefly glimpsed, rather than the past.

THE LADY IN BLACK

After midnight, when the constant din and commotion of the daytime has has been replaced with deathly stillness, the human mind is rather prone to that old after-dark enemy – the imagination. An over-active imagination was initially blamed when six-year-old Chloe from Mossley Hill woke up and found her bedroom door steadily opening at 2 o'clock on the Sunday morning of 12 August 2007. The girl peeped over the edge of her duvet and timidly asked, "Is that *you* mummy?"

No one answered but a woman in a long black dress suddenly peeped around the door. Her face was whiter than a sheet, and where her eyes should have been, there was nothing but empty black sockets. Chloe shivered, immediately realising, even at that tender age, that the stranger was a ghost. Then she let out a scream which brought her parents running into her room. Neither Chloe's mother nor her father saw any sign of the ghost in the room and thinking Chloe had simply experienced a nightmare, they tucked her up in bed and settled her back down to sleep.

However, that was not the end of the matter, for on the following night, the little girl was awakened by someone actually sitting on her bed. Again, it was the ghost with no eyes. Once again Chloe let out a scream before ducking under the duvet, and this time her mother and father caught a fleeting glimpse of the woman in black, as she vanished into a wall at the end of the landing. To my knowledge, the house in Mossley Hill where the night-prowling woman appeared had no reputation for being haunted, but Chloe's mother, Natalie, let slip a piece of information that quickly raised my suspicions.

In June of 2007, Natalie and her sister-in-law had decided to clear out the attic of the house, which was full of old junk, now of which belonged to them. They came upon a long black dress amongst the dusty piles of rubbish, and it looked as if it dated back to the 1970s. Upon touching this dress, Natalie heard a voice scream, "Get out of here!" The voice was also heard by Natalie's sister-in-law. At the same time, a strong current of air blew up from nowhere, showering cobwebs and dust in the women's faces, and they quickly left the attic, sensing that something paranormal was going on. They have not been back since.

It is a well known phenomenon, amongst people who know about such things, that the clothes of a deceased person can often be haunted by the person who once dressed in them. I recall an incident a few years ago involving a psychic young woman who was browsing amongst the secondhand clothes in Quiggins, when she happened to touch an old British colonel's jacket from the Second World War hanging on the rail. A loud gruff voice shouted out, "Don't touch me!" making her jump. The jacket in question was decorated with several war medals, and the girl received the strong impression that the spirit of its former wearer was bitterly disappointed at seeing his courageous and hard-won wartime achievements so belittled, that they had ended up in a secondhand clothes store.

The ghost haunting the Mossley Hill home had, in my opinion, been brought out of 'hibernation' by the disturbance of the black dress in the attic. A sleeping memory had been awakened. I have researched the history of the house by interviewing neighbours and examining electoral registers and I now believe that the woman in black is the sad phantom of a twenty-two-year-old woman called Miranda, who died at the house after a long illness in the 1970s. She was abandoned by her boyfriend just before her death, and attempted suicide twice. The love of her life, the person who kept her going, was a young sister whom she had visited whenever she could manage to drag herself up from her sickbed. The child also came to visit her, and when she did, she slept in the same room as the one in which Chloe now sleeps.

Hopefully the ghost of Miranda will settle down again soon and return to that strange limbo inhabited by restless ghosts.

THE PURPLE FLY ENCOUNTERS

Some readers may remember a game they played when they were children, in which you would stand on one side of a narrow road and throw a football at the opposite kerb, with the object of getting the ball to bounce back towards you from the kerb's edge. Your opponent, standing opposite you, attempted to catch the ball before it hit his kerb, and he would throw it back if he caught it, aiming at the kerb on your side of the road. The more inferior types of football would become squashed into an oval-shape when hitting the kerb, and this was colloquially known as having 'an egg in it'. The game was known by various names, including 'Kerby' and 'Sides'.

Anyway, this game was being played by Kevin and Michael, two eleven-year-olds from Childwall, one summer in 1979. It was Michael's turn and as he hurled the ball in an arc towards Kevin, something very peculiar happened. The ball struck what looked like an unusually large fly, which fell to the ground in the middle of the road.

"Uggh!" said Kevin. "What the heck was that?" and rushed over to stamp on the fly.

Michael however, had other ideas and stopped him.

"No! Don't! Let's have a look at it. It's really weird," he said.

The fly was unlike anything they had ever seen before. It was the colour of Tyrian purple, and when the boys squatted down and examined it closely, they could see that it had two human-shaped legs, as well as human-shaped arms, and a round head with a long pointed nose. The thing suddenly opened a pair of tiny diamond-like cobalt-blue eyes and emitted an odd buzzing noise, as if in warning. The boys drew back from the bizarre-looking insect and Kevin lifted the ball, ready to smash it down on the weird winged figure, but Michael seized the football from his friend and so saved its life. The purple fly unfurled its wings and flew off unsteadily into the clear blue sky and the children went back to their game and soon forgot all about the astonishing incident.

On the following day at school, during the dinner break, Michael was in the playground eating a bag of rainbow mixture acid drops, when the school bully Malcolm came up and slapped his face and swiped his bag of sweets.

"Hey! Give me them back, Malcolm, or I'll tell the teacher," cried Michael futilely. He knew full well that he would never dare try and get Malcolm into trouble; it was more than his life was worth.

Seconds later, a familiar purple speck appeared in the air right above the two children, just as Malcolm was stuffing three of the stolen acid drops into his mouth. Michael watched in amazement, and secret delight, as the funny-looking fly repeatedly attacked his tormentor, stabbing its pointed proboscis into his cheek. It then turned its attention to the bully's hand – the one that was clutching the bag of sweets – and started stinging it repeatedly. Malcolm dropped the sweets and fled into the school, howling with pain, and bounded into the medical room with agonising blisters erupting on his skin.

The purple fly spiralled in the air a few times, before ascending into the blue afternoon sky, as Michael looked up in awe. As he retrieved his sweets and popped one into his mouth, he tried to make sense of what he had just witnessed. He had never seen anything like it before in his life and never has since. So when he wrote to me a few years ago about the incident, he was surprised to learn that many of my readers had, over the years, contacted me with their own encounters with the purple fly.

Thirty-six year-old Tina, for example, told me how, in 1960, her three-year-old daughter often told her about a tiny little man with wings who visited her and talked to her as she played in the garden of her home on Heathfield Road. Tina had naturally assumed that the winged man was a figment of Tina's childish imagination – until she saw for herself a large purple fly, with distinctly odd appendages, hovering round her daughter on Penny Lane playing fields. Tina sketched this airborne enigma for me from memory and it looks uncannily similar to the entity which Michael and Kevin saw in 1979.

Another particularly fascinating case is that of reader Linda Hughes. She wrote that, in 1984, when she was twelve, for some reason she and her friends decided to explore the island in the middle of Childwall Fiveways Roundabout. They managed to get across the dangerous junction without mishap and there, sitting on a rock, was something purple with an angry-looking face and a pair of wings. The incredible insect, which was as big as her thumb, shouted something at the children with a chilling squeaky voice. Linda and her friends fled in fear and were almost knocked over by three oncoming vehicles.

What was behind all these mysterious sightings of the purple fly? Children can certainly anthropomorphise animals and insects, which is not surprising, since many children's stories involve animals who speak and behave like human beings. However, in some cases, adults also saw the odd-looking fly and remarked upon its long-nosed human-like face, as well as its miniature black human legs and arms. Many species of bluebottle and dragonfly have a metallic purple and indigo sheen (called pruinescence), but the purple fly seems very distinctive in shape, especially its bizarre appendages resembling human legs and arms, and those kinds of features are very difficult to explain away. The vividly-coloured Purple Skimmer dragonfly, which is native to Florida, could be mistaken as something magical to a British child, but how would such an insect, from a subtropical environment, manage to adapt to Liverpool's harsher climate, let alone get her in the first place?

I have a feeling that the truth is much probably more sinister. It is not difficult to speculate on the fly being an alien, or perhaps a creature from a parallel dimension. It remains a baffling mystery.

SHADOW PEOPLE

In my study I have a box-file labelled 'Shadows', which contains some fifty-odd letters from local people who have had chilling encounters with sinister silhouetted entities, that have been around since God knows when. Today, investigators of the paranormal across the world tend to call these mysterious beings Shadow People, but no one is entirely sure what they are and where they come from.

There are common factors in most reports of the Shadow People; the witnesses often experience a mounting sense of dread, and the rising of goose-bumps on their arms often presages the encounter, as does the unsettling – sometimes electrified – feeling of being watched when no one is about. The shadowy visitors usually appear at the edge of your field of vision, and when you turn to face them, they flit off to another place, or vanish altogether. Sometimes, though, they stand in full view and let you look right at them. Most people who have come across these humanoid silhouettes, can make out no discernible facial features; no mouth, no nose, no eyes, just blackness.

However, on one occasion, a Tuebrook woman saw a shadow person quite clearly; it was a man in a strange pointed black woollen cap, who appeared in her doorway gazing at the ground with a sad expression. As the frightened witness looked on, she noticed ink-like liquid dripping from the entity's eyes and rolling down its face. The figure then clasped its hands together, as if it was about to start praying, and then slowly faded away.

One of the earliest records of a Shadow Person took place at Number 37 Gwendoline Street, Toxteth, in 1895. A postman, Mr Lindsay, had lived quite happily at this address for a number of years, and during that time had never seen anything unusual or supernatural in his house. At 11.15pm on the evening of Saturday, 7 September, 1895, Mr Lindsay was sitting up in his bed, reading a book, because he did not feel at all drowsy, when he suddenly noticed something moving out of the corner of his eye. When he turned to look at it, he was astounded to see, on the wallpaper, the distinctive shadow of a man in a top hat and a coat with tails, kicking his legs up in the air as if he were dancing some kind of energetic Bohemian polka. The postman froze in trepidation as the dancing shadow skedaddled to a corner of the room, kicking its legs higher and higher, before it stopped abruptly and held its belly with both hands. It threw back its top-hatted head and its mouth opened as it guffawed silently. Then in a flash it was gone.

On the following morning, Mr Lindsay discovered that his next door neighbour, Mr Fowler's, lodger had died in his sleep at around 11.15pm. This unfortunate experience was not to be a one off event, and every time Mr Lindsay saw that dancing shadow on his walls, he could guarantee that he would hear news of a death very soon afterwards.

One of the most terrifying examples of the Shadow People was the menacing silhouetted face that apparently haunted many districts of Liverpool and Wirral in the 1970s. First there came a report from Sapphire Street, Wavertree, in 1973. Two boys, aged eleven and fourteen, saw the shadow of a "witch's face" in profile on their ceiling every night. This shadow-face would stay perfectly still for a while, then suddenly open and close its goofy mouth, as if it was speaking rapidly, although no sound could be heard. The ceiling ghost was also seen by the boys' parents and sister. An almost identical spooky shadow play was acted out on the ceiling of a bedroom at a house on Nimrod Street, Anfield, as well as on the wall of a young couple's bedroom at Damherham Mews, Belle Vale. Luckily, all of the nocturnal visitations were short-lived.

Over on Grove Road, Wallasey, in 2006, fourteen-year-old Megan was in her bedroom one evening at 10.30pm, gazing idly out of the window towards the nearby golf course, when she suddenly saw someone reflected in the pane. She turned reflexively and was startled to see a solid black shadow standing there, next to her wardrobe. The figure, apparently that of a man, was breathing heavily, yet she could see no details of any features in the silhouette – it was jet black – as if it were somehow a piece of the darkest night in the form of a person, was how Megan vividly described it.

The shock of the shadow man's sudden appearance in her bedroom triggered an asthma attack in Megan, and she quickly grabbed her inhaler. She exhaled fully, then depressed the canister between her lips and inhaled. As she did so, the shadow went out of focus and then vanished altogether. There was no way that Megan could go to bed after this and she sidled out of the room, keeping an eye out for the shadow man and then flew down the stairs, two at a time, only to find that her mother had gone out and left her in the house alone. She had gone to sit with a sick neighbour for a while, and her father was working nights at a factory in Little Sutton.

Megan had to get out of that house and therefore walked round to the house of the sick neighbour, a Mrs Stanley, who lived on Warren Drive, about five minutes away. When Megan's mother heard her daughter's bizarre account of the shadow she tried to explain it away as some kind of reflection, or trick of the light.

"No, Mum. It was nothing like that. You're not listening to me."

"Look, love. I think you're blowing this out of all proportion. You must have been dreaming. Isn't that right, Mrs Stanley."

"Yes, Meg. I remember when I was a girl. Always thought there was something out to get me the minute it went dark. Your Mum's right."

Having made her neighbour a hot drink and settled her down for the night, Megan's mother accompanied her daughter back to their house. She could see that the girl was still not herself, so she made her a cup of cocoa and went up with her to her bedroom to check that everything was as it should be. She checked under the bed and in the wardrobe.

"See! Everything's just fine. Now get into bed and get some sleep, Megan, or you won't want to get up for school in the morning."

"Okay, Mum. Night-night then."

"Night night, love. Now get some sleep."

Reassured, Megan was soon fast asleep, but that morning, at 4.45am, she woke up and immediately had the unnerving sensation of being watched. Her eyes nervously scanned the room, which was suffused with an orangey glow from the streetlights outside, and it was then that she saw the shadow man to her right, standing in the corner. She knew immediately that he was a ghost, because his lower half was occupying the same physical space as her sideboard. The girl squeezed her eyes tightly shut and got ready to shout for her mother – then she felt the bottom of her bed depress slightly – as if someone had just sat down on the end of the mattress. Megan kept her eyes closed and ran screaming out of the room and along the landing to her mother's room. She climbed on to her mother's bed and began shaking her, but her mother had been suffering from insomnia for the past few months, and had therefore taken a sleeping pill before retiring. "Mum! Wake up!" Megan shouted, shaking her mother violently by the shoulders, but she couldn't be roused.

The shadow man silently slithered after her into the bedroom and walked to the foot of the bed, apparently watching the frantic daughter and her unconscious mother. He began to reach out with his ink black shadowy hands towards Megan and she screamed to her mother at the top of her voice and even tried to force her eyelids open with her fingers. There came a low groaning from her mother as she grappled her way back into semi-consciousness. She gazed at the weird silhouette with a slightly puzzled expression and then asked who he was in a slurred voice. The figure vanished instantly.

When he returned home from his nightshift, Megan's father put the night's events down to his daughter's "overactive imagination", even though his wife said that she too recalled seeing a figure standing at the bottom of the bed, although she couldn't be one hundred per cent sure, because she had been so befuddled with the sleeping tablets. "You dreamt that," was her husband's blunt and candid explanation. But he would be made to eat his words, when, five days later, he saw the shadow man for himself, when he returned home from a late-shift at the factory one morning at four o'clock. As he entered the hallway, he saw what he at first assumed to be his wife standing at the top of the stairs in the semi-darkness, but when he looked again, he realised that it was the outline of a man.

"Who the hell are you?" he asked, at which the figure vanished in a heartbeat, before Megan's father could ask what he was doing in his house at that time of the morning.

The mysterious silhouetted stranger made a few more visitations to Megan's room after that night, but now seems to have retired from terrifying the schoolgirl and her parents.

Around the same time as the shadow man haunting in Wallasey, a twenty-two-year-old man called Andrew was serving his time at her Majesty's pleasure in Walton Prison. He woke up in his cell at around two o'clock in the morning to find the distinct shadow of a man on the ceiling, with a faint green glow surrounding the startling silhouette. He awakened his fellow cellmate and he too saw the ghostly shadow of a man drifting slowly across the ceiling for a duration of around two minutes. Then both the green glow and the shadow "went out like a light being turned off". Almost a week later, the same two prisoners saw the same shadow flit across the ceiling and then vanish into the cell wall, and on this occasion a faint hissing sound was also heard. As far as I know, the shadow person has not been seen since in that cell.

What exactly are these shadow people? Theories abound in ghost-hunting circles. Some believe they are simply bad spirits that cannot move on to the next world, whereas other researchers have speculated that the entities of darkness may be people in a neighbouring dimension, close to our own reality, who are being glimpsed distorted, or in negative light, for some reason. The most sinister theory concerning the shadow people conjectures that they are the work of witches who, through black magic, send the entities to harm their chosen victims. No one is really sure what these visitors are, or what they are seeking. What I would say from the number of reports I regularly receive regarding these spine-chilling apparitions, and from the volume of worldwide reports, is that the appearances of the shadow people are on the increase. The truth about their origin will almost certainly be revealed in the fullness of time.

THE TRAGIC GHOST OF NELLIE CLARK

Nellie Clarke was a highly-strung eleven-year-old girl who suffered from a disabling fear of the darkness, and she had a particular phobia about unlit alleyways and back entries. She lived at 16 Byrne Avenue, Rock Ferry, with her thirteen-year-old brother John and her mother, Sarah Good and stepfather, Peter Carr. Nellie's real father, John Wallace Clarke had been killed in France during the First World War.

Saturday, 10 January 1925 was quite an eventful day in the life of little Nellie. She had been invited to attend a special party given by the Lord Mayor for six hundred children who had been rendered fatherless by the war. The invitation was placed on the mantlepiece and she must have picked it up and looked at it over a hundred times a day.

At last, the great day arrived and she and her older brother John set off for the party, bubbling with excitement and dressed in their Sunday best. They each came home clutching a gift from the Lord Mayor himself. Nellie had received a beautiful doll, which she had christened 'Betty' and John had been given a gleaming chrome harmonica, the noise of which was driving his mother and stepfather quite mad, because he had no idea how to play it.

Nellie meanwhile, was happily playing with her new doll in front of the fire at 7.45pm that cold January Saturday evening, when her mother asked her to run an errand to the baker's shop. Nellie set off and then, as an afterthought, her mother told John to go after his sister, to tell her to bring some cakes back as well, and this he did. At around 8pm John and Nellie came back home together laughing and joking, each unaware that they would never see one another again in this lifetime. Nellie had just settled back into playing with her doll when she was sent out yet again, at around 8.10pm – to go on another errand to a shop at Number 201 Old Chester Road – and John asked his mother if he could go with her again.

"No, you'd better stay in this time," said Mrs Clarke sternly. "I don't want any larking about. When you two go out together, there's no knowing when you'll get back."

Sporting a red Tam o'shanter, and a red and white striped blouse frock under her brown winter coat, Nellie looked smart and cheerful, just as she usually did, when she called at the shop on the Old Chester Road. Having bought what her mother had asked for, she left the shop and set off for home – but the poor girl was destined never to get there. She had only minutes left to live before her innocence and her young life were about to be snuffed out by a predatory paedophile.

As the minutes and then the hours ticked away, Nellie's parents and brother naturally became deeply concerned for her safety. Mrs Carr and her son went out in search of Nellie but without success, yet they met with several people who had seen her that Saturday evening, including Lillian Smith, Nellie's classmate, who had seen her walking on her own towards the New Chester Road, a little distance apart from a group of children who were in front of her. That was at around 8pm, but Lillian couldn't be certain exactly what time it was.

At around 9.50pm, a Mrs Green, of Spenser Avenue, heard a loud bang at her front door, followed by a rattle of her letter-box. There followed a loud shriek, as if someone was in trouble – then nothing. Mrs Green rushed to the door but there was nobody to be seen and the avenue was eerily silent. Her young son, Robert, had also heard the spine-chilling scream, but he had heard more than his mother, for he had been startled by a girl's frantic voice crying out, "Father Christmas is after me! Let me in! Let me in!"

The search for Nellie Clarke went on into the early hours of the wintry Sunday morning, and at 8.25am, Martin Doran of Number 1 Highfield Grove, made a very grisly discovery – the body of a young girl propped up against a telegraph pole in the entry right outside his backyard. It was the ravaged body of Nellie Clarke. She had been raped and then strangled to death, and her body had been left in a passageway which she had scurried past many times, because of her fear of dark entries. There was a dark and discoloured oval mark under the girl's right ear, as well as various bruises on the left side of her throat, made by the fingers of the killer as he throttled the life out of her.

Mr Doran, the painter and decorator who discovered the body outside his backyard, had slept in the room overlooking the scene of the crime, yet he had heard nothing during the night, and stranger still, his dogs had not even barked in the yard at any time during that night, and those dogs were known to make the most awful din as soon as anyone came down the alleyway. The manager of Milne's Butchers Shop came forward and said that he had seen Nellie walking towards Bedford Street, Rock Ferry, with a smartly-dressed man of medium height. His description matched the one given by a taxi-driver who had picked up a fare at 10pm on the night of the murder. The man, whom he had never seen before, appeared to be agitated and almost barked at the cabby, "Take me to St Paul's Road – and quickly!" The cab-driver did as he was bid, but wondered to himself why the man was in such a hurry. Could he be trying to get away from the scene of a crime?

Later that night, after finishing his shift, he was having a quick drink in the nearby Royal Standard Hotel, when who should walk in but the suspicious customer he had picked up earlier. In the same gruff and demanding tone, he ordered a drink from the bar, gulped it down and then left without speaking to anyone. His appearance was not exceptional in any way; he was in his early forties, about five feet ten inches tall, smartly attired, quite slender and dark-haired. He was never seen again in the area after that night.

Mediums were consulted, but their 'information' was dismissed as useless. A bloodhound was also brought in, in the hunt for Nellie's killer, and after sniffing the dead girl's clothes to pick up her scent, it bolted off to waste ground close to the place were the child's body had been found and started to frantically scratch away at the soil. The dog uncovered a set of rosary beads that Nellie had lost weeks before her death. The dog then darted off down Rock Lane West and proceeded to another alleyway near some allotments behind Rock Ferry Congregational Church. When the bloodhound reached a corrugated iron sheet shed, which seemed to be being used as a tool store, it stopped dead, but for some reason the police failed to take this lead any further.

During the course of the investigation, an anonymous letter, written on distinctive pink notepaper, was sent to the police from one half of a courting couple who had been standing in the shadows of the entry off Spenser Avenue, where Nellie's body was dumped. The author of the letter, believed to have been a woman, said she and her beau had noticed an agile-looking man carrying a child in his arms as he passed by. They had both remarked on it but neither of them had been aware that the girl was missing at the time, so they had thought no more about it. The letter bore a Manchester postmark.

On 18 January that year, eight days after the Nellie Clarke murder, thirteen-year-old Lower Bebington schoolgirl, Edith Rose Colley, also went missing. Everyone quickly jumped to the same conclusion; that she had been murdered by the same monster who had killed young Nellie, and a massive search was launched. Then, two days later, Edith turned up alive and well. Apparently she had been aimlessly wandering about in Chester during the missing hours. Edith had written a goodbye note to her father before her disappearance – on pink writing paper. Her father was surprised at this, because he kept no pink stationery in his home, and was not aware that his daughter did either. The paper was of exactly the same type as that on which the anonymous letter from Manchester had been written. The police apparently didn't notice this, or make the important connection between the two notes.

Nellie Clarke's killer was never brought to secular justice – but I suspect that his maker has long since dealt with him. Many times over the years, the solid-looking ghost of Nellie Clarke has been spotted leaning against the same telegraph pole where her killer had abandoned her after he had molested and choked her to death. Some people claim that her tragic ghost still occasionally roams the streets of Rock Ferry where she used to play, and there have also been alleged sightings of the girl walking forlornly along Byrne Avenue, where she once lived.

HOODED HYPNOTIC GHOUL

Is there something inhuman and evil at large in Liverpool? I have received so many emails and snail-mail letters from all corners of the city, describing an entity which seems to be vampiric and downright malevolent in nature. Here are two of the fifteen reports I have received so far:

Just after 11pm on Wednesday, 14 February 2007, forty-three-year-old Elaine was walking homeward along Edge Lane, after a visit to her sister's house, when an "odd-looking man" wearing a hood approached her. Without greeting her in any way, he said "Smell this!" and offered her what Elaine took to be a Valentine's Day rose. The man's voice sounded soft and harmless, but she had no idea who he was, and it was eleven o'clock at night and she was out on her own. Deciding that the safest thing was to humour him, Elaine cautiously leaned forward to sniff the rose, and as she did so, she noticed that the stranger had a sinister, impossibly-wrinkled face. His round black eyes were like saucers, and were staring directly at her and between his open smiling lips she could see a frightening array of discoloured fanged teeth.

The grotesque character then roughly shoved the flower into Elaine's nostrils, and she felt a sharp prick inside her nose; there was obviously some sort of spike hidden in the rose's head. Elaine then felt a peculiar sensation of blood being drawn from her nose – as if the assailant was removing the blood through a syringe. Clutching her nose, she pushed the man away, then ran to the nearest door and hammered hard on the knocker. A man answered and when Elaine told him what had happened, he went in search of the hooded attacker but only managed to catch a glimpse of a figure in the distance running towards St Oswald's Street.

After the attack, Elaine realised that she might have been exposed to the HIV virus and so she volunteered to have the test. She had several anxious weeks to wait before she was told that she had not contracted AIDS from what she had assumed to be a hypodermic needle.

Then there was thirteen-year-old Robin, who, one day in June 2007, had been playing round Olive Mount, in Rathbone Road, and suddenly found himself hanging from a wall overlooking the railway track. Below him was a sheer drop of over a hundred feet. If he were to fall, he would not stand a chance. Fortunately, a passer-by heard his desperate cries for help and bravely rescued him from certain death. Robin's parents were furious at him for climbing the wall in the first place, yet the teenager had no recollection of how he came to end up so close to death. He didn't remember climbing the wall, and would never have done such a stupid thing – he wasn't that kind of lad.

Then the nightmares began. The boy suffered horrible, realistic dreams featuring a hooded man with a ghoulish, wizened face. The man held what looked like a plastic rose in his hand, and was beckoning the boy towards him with his index finger. In the dream, Robin found he was unable to resist the lure of his large hypnotic eyes, and he remained rooted to the spot as the menacing figure drew nearer. Then he felt a sharp stabbing pain in his lower lip, as the man thrust the rose up to his chin. The old man then ordered him to climb over the wall and jump on to the railway track below. At this point, Robin would usually wake up in his bed in a cold sweat.

A child psychologist was brought in, but could not be sure whether or not the whole thing was the product of the child's imagination, or whether he really had been attacked by such an assailant. The boy's parents now believe the latter, although they could find no evidence of needle puncture marks on their son.

I was struck by the almost identical descriptions of the man given by Elaine in the Edge Lane attack and the man Robin claimed haunted him in his nightmares. Both incidents are in fairly close proximity to one another, although very similar incidents reported to me have also taken place as far apart as Tuebrook, Anfield and Fazakerley. In each of these cases the witness mentions a hooded man of middle-height with a shrivelled, almost mummified face, and in the majority of the cases, he follows the witness home. In four out of the fifteen reports received over a period of almost a year, the ghoul successfully stabbed the victim with a pin, or hypodermic needle. I have discounted mass hysteria and other socio-psychological 'explanations', but I am not yet sure just what is behind these terrifying alleged attacks. Let's hope we have heard the last of them.

THE HAUNTED TELEVISION

A round 1969, there was a tavern on Hardman Street called O'Connors, and at that establishment one night in May, Ken and Bob, two brothers in their twenties, were enjoying a drink as they listened to the live music. Rob started talking about the latest episode in a popular television series, which featured a good old-fashioned beat bobby, called *Dixon of Dock Green*, and Ken was bemoaning the fact that his own television set was on the blink.

"I might be able to help you out there," said Rob.

"Don't tell me you've won the pools," laughed Ken.

"No, I found an old telly in our loft the other day. It takes a while to warm up, but the picture's fine. It's yours, if you want it."

"Great! Thanks Rob. I'm skint at the moment, so I can't afford a new one and it's so boring not having a telly."

On the following day, Rob brought the television set over to Ken's flat on Breck Road and plugged it in. The set gave off a rather dank and musky smell at first, but once it was used regularly, the aroma vanished.

One evening, a week later, Ken was in the middle of watching a war movie on the old television set, when after a commercial break, something strange and inexplicable took place. After the adverts had finished, and the war film had come back on, Ken noticed that colour was faintly suffusing the images on the screen. Now that should have been impossible, as it was a black and white television, but it was unmistakable. Colour television broadcasts had only just begun two years earlier, and the sets were still very expensive. This old set from Rob's attic should definitely not have been able to receive colour programmes, and yet here it was, in front of his eyes.

Ken also noticed that the actors in the film were suddenly nowhere to be seen, and had been replaced by oddly dressed soldiers with rifles, and they were firing at people. These people were not Germans, but civilians, and Ken could not make head nor tail of what was going on. What type of war movie was this? And how on earth had the scenes on the black and white television suddenly changed to vivid colour?

The sound from the television set seemed to surround Ken, engulfing him, as he watched in complete awe. He saw a young lad of about sixteen or seventeen years of age shaking from the impact of a bullet, then falling down on his back and coughing up blood. Ken trembled as he watched all this, and looked on with increasing confusion and incomprehension. He swore under his breath, "What the hell is this? What's going on?"

Horrible, gut-wrenching screams were now coming from the television, and Ken was barely able to look, as he watched another boy of about seventeen years of age catapulted backwards, as a bullet slammed into his stomach, killing him instantly. Ken then noticed another civilian – a middle-aged man – emerging cautiously from the side of a building, waving a white handkerchief at the soldiers. As he stepped out into the road, the back of his head exploded, and his brains spilled out on to the street. As well as the all too graphic violence, Ken was also quite shocked by the sounds of the people and the soldiers swearing profusely, and he wondered how the programme makers were getting away with all the profanities, as at that time swearing was only rarely heard on the television.

Ken turned away from the carnage and grabbed a copy of the *Liverpool Echo* to check the television listings page. He wanted to know what on earth it was that he was watching. All he could see was a war movie advertised for that time of night. About a further dozen people were shot to death during the course of that film, and the images were all violent in the extreme. About twenty minutes later, without warning, the picture returned to normal. The scenes being played out were once again in black and white, and suddenly two words appeared on the screen: THE END. The all too realistic war movie had ended and Ken was left feeling sickened by what he had seen. He also suspected that he had experienced something paranormal.

Ken went next door to his friend's house and asked him if he had seen the weird colour broadcast, with the uncharacteristically violent scenes, and his friend said that he had only seen an ordinary war movie, and that, of course, it had been in black and white, since he only had a black and white set. Ken also mentioned the shocking programme to his brother Rob and, in fact, to everyone he met, but no one else had seen it, or heard about it.

A few years later, in January 1972, Ken was watching the television news, when an item about a shocking incident which had taken place in Derry, Northern Ireland, was broadcast. Members of the 1st Battalion of the British Parachute Regiment had opened fire on unarmed civilians during a civil rights protest. Twenty-six people were shot, and thirteen people had been killed in the shameful incident. Six of the thirteen killed had been minors and five of the wounded had been shot in the back.

One of the civilians who had been shot dead had been waving a white handkerchief – and Ken immediately recognised him as the man he had seen on that old television set three years ago. During the following week, Ken read all that he could about the so-called Bloody Sunday massacre, and was left reeling when he recognised the faces of the dead in the newspapers.

He never saw any other visions of the future in that old television set, but he discovered that its previous owner, an old man by the name of McGowan, had reported seeing colour images of the Beatles on its screen around 1963, but he couldn't remember any more details.

The weird television set was stolen when Ken's flat was burgled in 1970, so it is possible that it is still out there transmitting its unique, real life dramas even today, perhaps to somebody who bought it 'off the back of a lorry'.

MANILU

D o vampires really exist? I have pondered that question so many times over the years. I remember taking calls at a radio station after a programme I had broadcast on vampires, and I talked to about a dozen callers who claimed that they had been bitten in the neck during the night, and had woken up with bloodstained pillows and bedclothes. A majority of these people lived close to one another off Earle Road, and I visited a few of these 'victims' and found them all apparently sane enough. These night-bites continued for about six months and then ceased as mysteriously as they had started.

Circulating around that time, was a persistent rumour about a vampire named 'Manilu', said to be on the prowl in the area around Lodge Lane. People came forward claiming to have actually seen him, and they described him as a bald-headed man with a pale, foreign-looking face, dressed in black. One sixty-seven-year-old woman told me how she had been walking along Hartington Road with her Jack Russell dog Simon one summer evening, at 10pm, when an odd-looking individual picked up the dog with both hands and sank his teeth into its flesh. The dog yelped and almost died from blood loss.

That same week in 1997, a man who matched the aforementioned description of Manilu, was seen prowling around Toxteth Park Cemetery, on Smithdown Road. A heroin-user, who often injected in the cemetery during twilight hours, told of a tall bald "ghoul" creeping amongst the gravestones, muttering to himself in a foreign language. A gang of children were roaming the cemetery several nights later when the tall oddity chased them, and allegedly grabbed one young lad by his ankle and threw him perilously high into the air as if he were a rag doll. On another occasion the heroin addict was spotted by the graveyard prowler, but he showed no interest in him, as if he instinctively realised that the drug user was not a threat, and simply walked off into the darkest reaches of the cemetery. Similar reports of Manilu date as far back as the 1940s, but probably much further, and may simply be urban legends, but I feel there is much more to him than that.

In 1894, sixty-year-old Emma Furnival, who ran a bakery at Number 13 Lodge Lane, was visited by an abnormally tall man in black with "foreign features" and peculiar sinister dark eyes. The man entered her shop to buy a loaf of bread, and spoke in broken English with an Eastern European inflection to his voice. At this time, rumours abounded of a vampire being at large in the south of Liverpool, after a child and a number of women living near Sefton Park had awakened in the morning to find strange puncture wounds on their necks. Bram Stoker had not yet written *Dracula*, his Gothic masterpiece, but the habits of vampires were already well-known, and one of their characteristic trademarks was the drawing of blood from the neck. The vampire was also widely believed to originate from Eastern Europe – from places such as Transylvania and Hungary. So when the tall thin foreigner with the staring eyes remarked upon the beauty of Mrs Furnival's neck, she immediately became so alarmed, that she dived through a door into the back room of the premises and locked herself in.

The man in the black homburg and frock-coat made himself scarce, but was later seen prowling about nearby Toxteth Park Cemetery at twilight. Two policemen chased him but he somehow managed to evade them amongst the forest of lichen-covered gravestones.

Weeks later, two spinster sisters, surnamed Bould, awoke at their home on Earle Road to find the tall silhouette of a man standing in their bedroom. One of the sisters screamed and fled from the room, but the other one remained in her bed, rooted to the spot with fear. The intruder assaulted her, biting into her neck, and drawing off blood, before fleeing through a window. The assailant was never captured, and his bloodsucking attack fuelled the vampire 'mania' prevalent in south Liverpool at that time.

To the relief of all concerned, the reports of the vampiric man then subsided for over half a century, but in the late 1940s, dark murmurings about a vampire who prowled the area bounded by Lodge Lane, Smithdown Road and Ullet Road began to circulate in postwar Liverpool. According to the rumours, the vampire was well over six feet in height, and had revealed his name to be – Manilu – and some said his first name was Nathan. He was said to have lived at a crumbling Victorian house off Lodge Lane for over forty years, and at this abode he had accumulated a handful of loyal disciples, who had been initiated into his personal religion by participating in blood-drinking rites. Of course, the vampire stories may be nothing more than hearsay, urban myths and exaggeration, yet from the evidence I have gathered, I believe there is more than a grain of truth in the stories of Manilu.

In the 1980s, a wave of vampire reports rippled across several parts of Liverpool, again originating in Lodge Lane. A highly-controversial self-styled vampire-hunter, Victor Mordelly, set out to confront the vampire and permanently lay it to rest. Equipped with hawthorn stakes, holy water, crucifixes – and a profound knowledge of these creatures of the night – Mordelly allegedly traced Manilu to his lair. I will now relate the shocking outcome of this vampire hunt, according to Mordelly's own testimony.

In February 1983, a young single mum living in a bedsit off Lodge Lane, with her eight-month-old baby, had the feeling that she was being watched. She was not the superstitious or paranoid type, but from the day she moved into the bedsit, she had had the horrible sensation of being observed by someone or something next door, especially at night. In the end, the atmosphere in the bedsit became so intensely edgy, that she couldn't stand it any longer. She took the baby from its cot and set off for Wavertree Road Police Station and there she told a sceptical constable about the interminable feeling of being watched by something evil in the flat next door.

The policeman was sympathetic, because he could see how distraught she was, but said that regrettably, there was nothing he could do. Upon which, the girl began to sob, and when she started, so did her baby. She hysterically begged him to send an officer to the flat adjacent to her bedsit, because she was convinced that something sinister was going on next door – but it was difficult for her to put her fears into words. To calm her down, and get her and her crying infant out of the police station, the desk sergeant promised to send someone round to look into the matter. This reassured her and she bundled the baby back into its pram and set off back to the bedsit.

That night, as the young woman was watching *News at Ten* to take her mind off her eerie predicament, she was startled by loud thumps coming from the flat next door. She looked out of the window and saw a police car down below in the street. She realised, with a sigh of relief, that the police had responded to her plea, and were inspecting the next-door flat; they had been the source of the banging noises. Her assessment of the situation was correct and the police later revealed to her what they had found in the flat, and the revelation resulted in the girl packing her bags on the spot.

The first thing that struck them after they had broken into the flat, was that the previous occupant had painted all of the walls black and they were dotted with mysterious pentagrams and other occult symbols. In the middle of the floor there was a coffin, which was encrusted with mould and earth and looked at least a hundred years old. It had probably been stolen from one of the tombs in the local graveyard, but it was found to be empty and there were no traces of the corpse it had once contained. The nameplate was too rusted and eaten away by the soil to be identifiable. Lying next to the coffin, was an ancient mildewed handwritten book on occultism, entitled *The Lord of the Gales* – and next to this tome was an empty milk bottle – which contained a small amount of clotted human blood!

No one in the street could remember having seen anyone entering or leaving the flat, so it was impossible to identify or trace the missing occupant, and he or she never returned. Even the hard-boiled streetwise policemen admitted that they had experienced an icy chill in that flat. Understandably, the young mum left the bedsit that very night and went to stay with her aunt on the Wirral.

The fifty-year-old self-styled 'vampire-hunter', Victor Mordelly, committed the crime of trespass to investigate this peculiar incident and examined every inch of that flat. He looked into an empty wardrobe and discovered a hole in its base, which again led into a hole in the floorboards. This hole led down into the cellar, and from the cellar, a tunnel ran away into the darkness. The courageous Mr Mordelly set out to explore this tunnel, armed with his vampire-hunting kit, which contained a mallet, hawthorn stakes, holy water, cloves of garlic, and a crucifix.

He bravely negotiated the winding tunnel for a mile, or maybe two, until he came upon a large vault coated with fungus and lichens and hung about with tiny stalagmites and stalactites. Set into the limestone-encrusted floor of this vault, was a large block of sandstone, upon which someone had placed two rusted candlesticks streaked with black wax.

Mordelly had seen such subterranean 'altars' before in the tunnels leading from Beeston Castle in Cheshire, as well as in the caverns beneath places as far apart as Billinge and Kirkby Lonsdale. He detected tell-tale dark stains of mammalian blood on the altar, but no sign of the Sanguinarians (Mordelly's term for vampires) responsible for the sacrifices.

The fearless vampire stalker raked the darkness which stretched out ahead of him with the beam of his torch, as he trudged through a tunnel that became increasingly waterlogged with each step. After almost an hour he came upon a glimmer of light in the roof of the tunnel. Pale wintry daylight bled in through a crescent-shaped opening in the roof, and Mordelly recognised the grim grey tenements known as Fontenoy Gardens through the aperture. He consulted his *A to Z* map book and deduced that the secret passage had led him into a disused railway tunnel. The only exit from this tunnel was blocked by a landslide of discarded rubbish, so Mordelly was forced to retrace his steps. When he passed the altar for the second time, he heard a noise reverberating through the tunnel, and at first it sounded like the dripping of water, which had percolated down through the sandstone stratum. Clouds of his exhaled breath bloomed in mid-air in the glare of the torch as his anxiety mounted – then he saw Manilu.

Mordelly claims in his unpublished books on vampirology that some of these underground bloodsuckers living in perpetual darkness were devoid of eyes, but the vampire standing inert before him had very large expressive eyes, which were red and watery. Mordelly slowly reached into his satchel to retrieve a revolver already loaded with hollow-point bullets and tainted with hawthorn berry powder. With an extraordinary swiftness, the vampire flew at him, knocking him on to his back with a bony fist. The thing held him down by the throat and bared its long fangs.

Mordelly lay helplessly on his back, with the iron grip of the blood-sucking fiend Manilu around his neck. He could scarcely breathe. The vampire knelt with his legs on either side of Mordelly as he opened his mouth like a snake, ready to pierce the carotid artery. Seconds away from choking to death, Mordelly felt the ground in desperation, praying to find the revolver loaded with hawthorn-tipped bullets, but it wasn't there. Instead, Mordelly's hand located his sharpened hawthorn stake, and in one swift movement, he rammed its pointed end into the vampire's gaping mouth, until it was impaled deep in the palate.

The creature's agonised screams echoed through the labyrinth, as blood dripped and sprayed from its mouth. It was forced to release its deadly grip and then reared up, frantically trying to wrench out the stake. Mordelly pushed the soles of his boots into Manilu's chest and sent him flying backwards into the gloom. He then spotted the revolver by the light of the torch lying in a puddle, and he seized it and began to fire shots at the bloodsucker. After the third shot the unearthly figure flitted away into the shadows, with the agility of a startled spider. Mordelly turned and ran for his life back down the tunnel, until at last he reached the familiar cellar of the house off Lodge Lane. He knew that he had had a very lucky escape.

Mordelly then rented a flat on Picton Road in Wavertree, and there he wrote an account of his encounter with various vampires in Liverpool and elsewhere. He approached a local paranormal investigation group and asked them to assist him in his vampire hunt, but they mocked him and decided he was crazy. Mordelly claimed to have found evidence showing that the vast network of tunnels excavated by the 'Edge Hill Mole', Joseph Williamson, under the streets of Liverpool in the early 1800s, had now been overrun by light-fearing vampires. Even more controversially, he suggested that Williamson himself may have been a dhampir (having a vampire father and human mother).

John Burns, a member of the ghost-hunting group, initially believed Mordelly was a crank, until late one night in 1983, when he pulled into a filling station in Wavertree. Burns saw Mordelly running from a lane, pursued by two strange-looking men in black – each about six foot five inches in height. Burns watched as one of these tall skinny men picked up Mordelly as if were a feather and threw him on to a skip full of rubbish. Burns rushed to Mordelly's aid and so was able to see, from closer quarters, that the eccentric man's attackers were pasty-faced with joined-up eyebrows and long pointed fangs.

One of the sinister figures lunged towards Burns, and was about to sink his fangs into him when he was struck by a car. Despite receiving appalling injuries in the collision, the lanky figure leapt to its feet and gave chase, along with its weird-looking comrade. Mordelly ran with Burns to his car and they managed to escape in the nick of time.

According to Mordelly, the two figures were centuries-old vampire confederates of Manilu.

After that night, Burns saw Mordelly in a new light; he was not a crank at all, but a serious and courageous vampire detective. He decided to join him in his quest to fight the Sanguinarians. I could fill a book with the tales of Mordelly and Burns, and who knows, perhaps one day I will, although I doubt that many people would believe my accounts of their hair-raising nocturnal adventures.

Believe it or not, vampires are still being reported to this day. In January 2005, vampire mania swept through Birmingham, after the newspapers reported a Dracula-like attacker on the loose. The 'Birmingham vampire' was even reported in the high-brow pages of *The Guardian* newspaper. The vampire reports are also available to see online.

According to Mordelly, Manilu is still at large across the North West after nightfall. I remember an incident many years ago, in the 1990s, in which a Tuebrook man walked to a filling station, at three o'clock in the morning, to buy cigarettes, and whilst on his way, a black limousine pulled up, and two tall men in black suits seized him by each elbow and manhandled him into the back of the vehicle. The man fiercely resisted at first but then felt an electrical jolt shooting through his chest; perhaps from a stunner. He became groggy and disorientated as the limo was driven to somewhere in the Toxteth area, the captive knew that much, because he remembered passing Lodge Lane Library.

The abducted man was taken into a house and forced down into a spacious cellar, where a man was sitting on what could only be described as a throne. It was a high-backed seat of marble, featuring strange gargoyles and carvings of serpents. The man seated on it was completely bald, and although he was sitting down, it was clear from the unusually elongated proportions of his torso and limbs, that he was exceptionally tall. His face was so pale that it looked as if he was wearing make-up, and his eyes protruded grotesquely from their dark-lined sockets. On one of his fingers he wore a large ruby ring, and his suit looked as if it was made of black velvet. His shirt was dark blue and gleamed like heavy satin. For a few tense moments he surveyed the captured man trembling between the two heavies before him, then announced, "That is not Cavaleri" (or what sounded like that name).

The man on the throne waved the frightened Tuebrook abductee away and the two tall muscular henchmen dragged him back up a flight of stone steps and into the limousine. The man was dropped off on Binns Road without a word of explanation or apology. The gargoyles and serpents on the throne indicate an occult element. Is it possible that the man seated on that throne was the legendary and elusive Manilu?

RENSHAW STREET RIDDLE

G hosts that harm are exceptionally rare. Poltergeists have occasionally inflicted wounds by throwing heavy objects at people (and I have a scar in my hand from such an entity, that drove a nail into my left palm during a haunting at Speke, many years back) but on the whole, things from the 'other side' are mostly benign. However, a certain distinctive phantom that has been known to wreak serious, sometimes almost fatal injuries, started doing his rounds again in Liverpool in April 2007.

This solid-looking carnate apparition was reported as far back as the 1920s, and always makes its appearance in a spectacularly dramatic fashion. Rumbling sounds are heard, often accompanied by strange-sounding chimes. A scent of violets frequently fills the air and all of this heralds the appearance of a point of light in a wall, or sometimes in mid-air. A 'hole' opens up from this luminous point, to reveal a long tunnel of blue light, and from this supernatural passage, a top-hatted man in a long flowing cloak emerges.

In 1922, this ghost appeared in just such a fashion in the cellar of a shop on Renshaw Street, close to the corner of Leece Street. The proprietor of the shop, a man named Parry, went down into his cellar after hearing a loud commotion, and there he witnessed an eerie materialisation. His instinct told him to get out of there as fast as his legs could carry him. As he turned to flee back up the stairs, the Victorian-looking manifestation struck him hard on the head with the handle of a walking cane, knocking him clean out. When Parry regained consciousness, the violent ghost was nowhere to be seen.

The mystery deepened when Parry and several of his friends discovered secret passages leading from the cellar in the Renshaw Street shop. These passages still exist, but their entrances have been bricked up. In the late 1980s and early 1990s, a Kwik Fit garage stood on the site of Parry's shop, and there were many sightings there of the top-hatted man coming up into the garage from the cellar. Neither did the ghost confine its terrifying antics to that location; it also appeared in the basements of

Central Hall, as well as the cellar of a local pub.

On Monday 2 April 2007, this sinister aggressive spectre was out on the prowl again. It was seen at 11pm, striding along nearby Benson Street by a hackney cab driver who was shocked to see the figure vanish into a wall. A man who has a shop on Renshaw Street saw the very same figure in a top hat and a long billowing opera cloak, twirling a walking cane as it walked down Heathfield Street – and that was in broad daylight. Could it just have been a belated April Fools Day prank? or someone off to a fancy dress party? I don't think so – not unless the joker had the ability to walk straight through solid walls and dematerialise at will, because this gent in Victorian clothes strode into a wall near a Rapid Hardware store.

An exorcist I have known for many years was called out to confront the cocky ghost, after it appeared in a basement at Grand Central (formerly Central Hall) on Renshaw Street, and he claimed his right hand was fractured after the ghost swung its cane at him. He showed me the plaster cast on his hand as proof. A medium I consulted said that he felt the ghost's surname was Byrom, and that he was a practising occultist in his day, who was determined to defeat death when his time was up. I dug deep and consulted the archives to discover that one John Byrom, an eccentric violin manufacturer, once lived at Number 37 Renshaw Street in the 1890s. Could this be our ghost? I wondered.

There are extensive but poorly mapped tunnel systems under Renshaw Street and the neighbouring streets, but during the ghostly antics of the violent phantom, I received an email from Mike Clarke, the spokesman of a group of amateur underground explorers, known as the Subterraneans, who, as their name suggests, investigate the forgotten warrens, catacombs and labyrinths of tunnels that exist beneath the streets of Liverpool. Mr Clarke told me that the top-hatted ghost which had been seen at various places on Renshaw Street, had also been seen strutting along a tunnel that runs close to the cellar of the Dispensary public house, to a vault near a disused graveyard at the back of Grand Central Hall – formerly Central Hall.

Callie, a nineteen-year-old member of the Subterraneans, was exploring an offshoot of a tunnel that runs from Renshaw Street to Lime Street, when she heard footsteps behind her. She turned to train her high-powered torch on the origin of the footsteps, and the beam illuminated a tall man in a top hat with a long black cape, striding towards her as he twirled a walking cane. Callie ran away from him, but tripped and fell face down in a puddle of rainwater that had seeped into the tunnel. Fortunately, on this occasion, the menacing figure marched straight past her and vanished into the darkness.

On the afternoon of Wednesday 9 May, Julie, who runs Morgana's Lair – a popular shop at Grand Central that sells Gothic dresses, pagan jewellery, and Wiccan paraphernalia – was approached by a stranger dressed in the very same attire as the ominous figure seen by Callie in the Renshaw Street tunnel.

"At first I thought he was a customer," says Julie, "as it's not unusual for shoppers to dress in Victorian gothic attire, but when he reached the top of the stairs leading to Morgana's Lair, my blood ran cold, because I saw that the man had an indistinct hazy face; vaporous almost. I sensed he was something evil from way back in time. He approached pointing a walking cane at me in his raised hand, and I reflexively picked up a besom – a charm in the form of a small broomstick that had been given to me a few years ago. The charm is used by Wiccans to sweep away negative energies. Holding the besom before me, I watched as the weird figure suddenly stopped dead in its tracks. It turned around and went back the way it came."

Julie did not see this ghost reach the bottom of the steps, but other people in Grand Central subsequently reported a profusion of cold spots at various points around the building.

The ghost made a brief reappearance at a hat shop in Grand Central, in August 2007, before going into a period of hibernation. This is a common practice amongst ghosts; they may lie dormant for years, decades even, and then come out of the woodwork for a while, before returning to their curious limbo. A medium who is investigating the Renshaw Street ghost tells me the entity haunting Grand Central is the spirit of a late-Victorian occultist, who was 'summoned forth' by dabblers in so-called 'Dark Side Magick' around Easter 2007. We may discover more about this intriguing ghost in the future, and who knows, reader, you may even bump into him yourself when you're next in the Renshaw Street area …

THE FACELESS ONES

Of all the various types of ghost I have investigated over the years, I would say that the ones with no face are the most disturbing. Our entire character lies in our face, and so to be confronted with a face as smooth and featureless as an eggshell, can be very unnerving.

In the 1970s, the solid-looking ghost of a girl with no face haunted the Walton Hall Park area of the city, and one of the first people to report the apparition was a cab-driver, who saw a lonely looking girl of about fourteen years of age, standing forlornly at the kerbside on Rice Lane at a quarter to midnight. Rain was falling hard and the girl looked drenched to the bone, so the cabby pulled over and leaned towards the nearside window to wind it down, but he froze when he suddenly noticed that the girl had no face. She had long dripping-wet hair and wore no coat of any kind, just a thin pullover. She had a completely blank face, smooth and devoid of any eyes nose or mouth.

The taxi-driver drove off at high speed and was so shaken up by his experience, that he almost crashed his taxi at the corner of Grey Road. A policeman on the Walton Hall Avenue beat, was one of the next people to have an encounter with the faceless girl, but unlike the taxi driver, he bravely stood his ground. The meeting took place two weeks after the incident with the cabby, near Blackthorne Road, adjacent to the grounds of Walton Hall Park, at 11.15pm, and once again it was raining heavily. The girl came from the direction of Richard Kelly Drive, and initially the policeman thought she was a living person, until he stopped to ask her why she was out on her own at such a late hour. The girl's long hair covered most of her face, but when she turned to confront the policeman, he was stunned to see nothing but a flesh-coloured ovoid, lacking any hint of any features from her forehead to her chin.

The constable was naturally disturbed by her unique appearance, yet at the same time, he felt a strong sympathy for the girl, whose whole body seemed to give off an air of deep sadness and dejection. He tried to catch up with her as she ran off under a nearby railway bridge, but as he approached her, she vanished into thin air, and simultaneously the sound of her footfalls ceased. The ghost of the blank-faced girl has been seen intermittently in the area over the years, and no one has any idea whose phantom it is.

* * *

Equally anonymous, is the ghost of the faceless woman who has haunted Moss Street, London Road and Pembroke Place since the 1980s. He face has been described as a pale, featureless oval and from her attire (a very short skirt and high stiletto heels) some people have drawn the conclusion that she is the ghost of a prostitute who was murdered in the area many years ago. This faceless woman was walking along Moss Street in 2002, when a bus 'hit' her. Many passengers and pedestrians witnessed the collision, and naturally assumed that a real person– albeit a very strange one – had been knocked down. Yet when they went to her aid, there was no body to be found.

In another sighting, a man claimed that she had walked up to the Spiritualist Church on Daulby Street one night and entered that building by passing through a solid brick wall. And a policeman who attended one of my talks on the supernatural told me that a kerb-crawler reversed into a lamp-post on Pembroke Place one night, after mistaking the ghost for a prostitute!

In August 2005, the faceless ghost was seen on Crown Street over several evenings by different groups of students. Just why the ghost decided to hang about in an area, away from its usual haunting grounds, is unknown, but weeks after its appearance, Kensington grandmother Anne Marie Foy, was murdered on that stretch of Crown Street. She was savagely beaten and strangled and left in bushes at the spot.

* * *

The apparition of a young faceless boy is said to have haunted Ogden's Tobacco Warehouse for many years, and is thought to be the ghost of an orphan who had his face badly burned during a fire at St George's Catholic Industrial School for Boys, on West Derby Road, in the nineteenth century. Industrial schools were created for the children of feckless or absentee parents and their regimes were harsh and uncompromising, designed to prepare the inmates for a life of honest toil. Children died in great numbers within the walls of such grim institutions and many ghosts from that orphanage haunted Ogden's.

* * *

Surely one of the most terrifying faceless apparitions to haunt Liverpool was the phantom passenger who often appeared on the top deck of the Number 79 bus, as it travelled through Childwall, Wavertree and Edge Hill, en route to the city centre. It was first seen by a bus driver named Norman, who noticed a strange-looking passenger through his periscope as he drove down Picton Road. It was to be the first of many sightings. The smartly-dressed man had a mop of curly grey hair, but no face, and he always seemed to appear in the Childwall area. At the terminus, Norman would wait for his peculiar character to disembark, so that he could get a better look at him, but he never came down the stairs.

In the end, a medium was enlisted to help sort out the mystery and allay the driver's fears. The medium ascertained that the ghost was an earthbound spirit, who had died whilst suffering partial memory loss and had forgotten who it was and what it looked like. The bus was eventually blessed by a priest and the ghost disembarked for good.

THE BALLERINA

One November evening, in 1975, at a terraced house in the district of Norris Green, Mrs Janet Armitage was sitting in her favourite fireside armchair, holding a copy of the *Daily Mirror*, absorbed with her horoscope as described in the column of trusted astrologer, Patrick Walker. Suddenly, she heard an unusual noise on the stairs. She crept out of the front parlour, imagining that she would catch one of her young daughters sneaking back into the house without telling her, but instead, she found something much more disquieting. What could only be described as a scarlet pool of blood was slithering *up* the bare wooden stairs. The stairs were bare because the carpet had been removed from them on the previous day, because it was so worn and frayed.

Mrs Armitage stared uncomprehendingly at the upwardly mobile pool of blood for a few moments, before retreating into the parlour, feeling weak at the knees. She called out to her slumbering overweight mongrel dog Jerry (named after the pop-blues band Mungo Jerry five years before) but the hound's head was lying on his one good ear and so he slept on. Janet shook him awake and dragged him by his collar to the door of the parlour, then opened it and coaxed the sleepy and reluctant Jerry into the hallway with her slippered foot. She then turned on the light in the hallway, grabbed her coat, opened the front door, and stood on the step, gazing back at the docile dog, who was staring back at her with a sluggishly wagging tail.

Janet had often remarked on how useless Jerry was as a guard dog and had once joked that, if robbers got in the house to break into the gas meter, Jerry would hold the torch for them. It was 9.15pm, and Janet expected her two wayward daughters – Valerie, aged fourteen, and Samantha, aged thirteen – to come sauntering down the street at any minute. Instead, John – the husband from whom she was separated – came to visit, drunk as usual, whingeing on about how much he missed her, and suggesting she should come with him to the local pub. Even under the present circumstances, Janet wouldn't consider letting him cross the threshold, as she had had more than enough of his drunken ways throughout the past sixteen years. Not being a woman to mince her words, she told him to get lost.

John ended up staggering off down one end of the street, as his daughters came sauntering home from the other. Mrs Armitage raised her thumb and gestured for her girls to get indoors promptly. Valerie, dressed from head to foot in her Bay City Roller's tartan, and Samantha, still dressed in her school uniform, hurried into the house deep in conversation about the lads they had been with and barely noticed their frantic mother. Valerie went straight into the kitchen and opened a bag of her favourite Bovril-flavoured crisps and Samantha, or Sam, as her sister and mother called her, went straight to the mirror to take a close look at a spot on her nose which one of the boys had teased her about. Mrs Armitage didn't dare mention the crawling pool of blood she had seen on the stairs, as both girls were very highly strung and were not even allowed to watch the b-movie horror films on late-night television, because anything supernatural tended to play on their minds.

That night, at around 11.30pm, Janet was about to go to bed, when her husband called at the house again. He tried to let himself in with his key but Janet had bolted the door, and through the letterbox she shouted at him to go home and leave her in peace. John Armitage stood there, swaying on the doorstep, holding a half-eaten parcel of fish and chips, virtually unable to speak because he was so drunk. Janet bawled at him and after a few harsh words had been exchanged, Mr Armitage staggered off in search of a taxi to take him to his one-bedroom flat in Anfield. However, their parents' noisy squabbling had woken the girls, and a sleepy Samantha shouted down to her mother: "Was that me dad, mam?"

"No, go back to sleep!"

Samantha was unable to go back to sleep, though, as she was one of those people who found it hard to return to sleep once she had been woken up in the night. She sat up in bed, screwed up her eyes, and focused on her sister, who was sleeping peacefully across the room in the other bed. Samantha was bored and was itching to wake her under some pretence, but she knew that Valerie cherished her sleep and was always very grumpy and nasty to her when her sleep was disturbed.

So, thinking better of it, Sam lay back in her bed and idly gazed at the distorted squares of faint orange streetlamp light being projected on to the ceiling through the window panes. It was then that she saw the black thing crawl slowly across the ceiling from left to right. At first Sam thought it was the shadow of something on the window – perhaps a leaf blown by the wind – but the amorphous object emitted a faint hissing sound as it split into two, and each half then slid around the plaster rose on the ceiling above the lampshade. The thing looked as if it were made of some kind of viscous liquid, like oil, or treacle. The two halves then joined up again on the other side of the rose, and the moving 'puddle' of darkness started sliding across the ceiling and moving steadily down the wall.

Sam had never been so afraid of anything before. She felt breathless and couldn't even raise the tiniest squeak. Yet even though she was numb with fear, she somehow managed to stay upright.

Now the thing was on her bed!

She managed to let out a scream, at which the black flat oval puddle glided sideways over the covers of her bed and dropped on to the carpet with a dull thump. Sam's scream and the noise from the thing were enough to wake up Valerie. She opened her eyes, confused for a moment, then sat up and looked over at Sam, who was now quaking under her blankets.

"Sam, what's wrong?" asked Valerie, jumping out of the bed. As she did so she saw something too fast for her eye to discern, as it zipped across the carpet and disappeared under the bedroom door. Valerie prised the covers off her sister and once again asked her what the matter was.

Sam flung her arms around her older sister and clung to her.

"There was this ... this thing on my bed ... it was horrible ... and now it's on the floor!"

The door flew open and both girls jumped.

"What's all this screaming for?"

It was their mother, Janet. She switched on the light and stood there in her curlers and faded old nightie, and her eyelids looked glued together and in need of sleep.

"I said what's all the screaming for?" she repeated. "You look as if you've seen a ghost, Sam."

Sam still clung on to Valerie, as she leaned sideways ever so slightly and looked down at the floor to check whether the 'thing' was still about. Thank goodness it wasn't. She then gave her account of what she had seen, and her mother shuddered, because she recalled only too vividly the slimy slippery thing that she had seen earlier in the evening slithering up the stairs. Valerie added credence to Sam's account by mentioning the flitting shadow that had disappeared under the gap in the bedroom door.

As you can imagine, none of the three women got much sleep that night, and not until the reassuring light of dawn broke over Norris Green, did any one of them dare to even close their eyes. The exhausted girls were given that morning off school, and their mum wrote two explanatory notes for them to take to their form teachers in the afternoon.

At 1pm that day, when the girls had left for school, John Armitage called round at the house with a bunch of flowers, slightly bedraggled flowers, it has to be said, but bringing any sort of flowers was certainly out of character for him. This did the trick, and Janet allowed him in for a cup of tea, "and that's all John", she warned him. She told him about the night's unbelievable events, knowing that he would be interested, because her husband was not only keen on spirits of the alcoholic kind, but also had a long-standing interest in the supernatural. When sober, John was the kindest, most considerate and intelligent man Janet knew, and it was so lovely to be able to sit down and have an intelligent conversation with him when in such a state of sobriety. She told him this and a tear bled from his eye, and he nodded.

"I know Jan," he sighed, and then took a large gulp of his tea. He stood up, trying to hide his emotions, and said, as a way of changing the subject, "These ghosts that just start haunting a place are usually spirits that have been disturbed."

"How do you mean?" Jan asked, lighting a cigarette.

"Well have you been clearing out any rooms, or altering the place at all? Decorating, that sort of thing?" John stood in the doorway of the parlour as he said these words, eyeing the bare stairs in the hallway.

"Well yes, I suppose I have, in a way. I just took up the carpet on the stairs, because it was all frayed. Is that what you mean." Jan rose from the table, puffing on a Players cigarette and looked into the hallway – then suddenly she remembered something. "Oh, hang on a minute. Now I come to think of it, I cleared the attic out last Tuesday."

"What for?" asked John. "Were you looking for something?"

"No. The girls thought they heard rats, so I threw out a lot of that rubbish that was in there. It'd been there since we moved in and I was always asking you to sling it out, if you remember," said Janet. "I got rid of about half of it, but it was so filthy and dusty up there, that I left the rest."

"Is it okay if I take a look?" asked John, standing on the bottom step, with his hand resting on the large square acorn cap of the handrail.

"Yeah, be my guest, if you think it will help."

Fifteen minutes later, John and Janet were up in the attic. The grimy cobwebbed window admitted the soft glow of daylight from the overcast afternoon sky, and by that dreary radiance, John sifted through a stack of old framed pictures in the corner, as Janet rooted through a battered chest stocked with dented tins of Mansion Polish, a metal box containing a ball of string, wire wool pads, old wooden pegs, and a can of Brasso metal polish.

John took out a handkerchief and dusted the glass of a silver-framed picture he had found. It depicted a ballerina, but the painting was unsigned. As John and Jan looked at the painting, they both heard a brief snatch of very faint music playing in the attic. The instrument sounded like a celesta, and was vaguely familiar. Janet thought long and hard about the music and eventually she recognised it. It was the 'Dance of the Sugar Plum Fairy' from Tchaikovsky's fairy-tale ballet, *The Nutcracker*.

"Sam would like that," said John and Jan simultaneously, referring to the ballet dancer painting. They both gave a short laugh at their synchronised remarks, then again thought about that eerie music. They both felt a little uneasy after the incident, and left the attic feeling that they had stirred up more questions than answers.

At 2.15pm that afternoon, John hung the picture of the ballerina in the girls' bedroom. Sam had always wanted to be a ballet dancer, and John hoped his daughter would like it. He left her and his other daughter some money to buy sweets and magazines, then kissed his wife and returned to Anfield, filled with regret at what he had lost through his unhealthy relationship with drink.

At 4.15pm the girls came home and were a little sad when they learned that their father had been to the house and gone home without seeing them, but they used the money he had left them to buy copies of *Jackie* and *Look-In* magazines, as well as a mountain of sweets. Sam loved the painting of the ballerina and started to annoy Valerie by dancing around the bedroom en pointe to a T Rex number on her record player. By now they had almost forgotten the strange events of the night before, but when bedtime loomed, Sam started to sob quietly.

"I don't want to go to bed. What if it comes again?" she said. "I'm scared, really scared."

"Look, don't be so daft," said Valerie. "It was probably only a nightmare."

"But you said you saw it too!" Samantha reminded her sister.

"I don't know what I saw," Valerie said solemnly. "Now I come to think about it, it was probably just a mouse."

That night the girls sang pop songs to each other as they lay in their beds and Sam flashed her multi-coloured torch around, until, at 11.15pm, their mother shouted up to their bedroom for them to be quiet and get some sleep. Samantha and Valerie whispered about boys and friends at school for a while, until gradually, at almost half-past midnight, they both drifted off into that mysterious world of dreams.

At around 3am, Sam woke up, and heard a strange noise. She froze, imagining it was the slithering puddle of shadow, but when she calmed down a little, she realised it was merely the sound of rain pattering on the window. She turned in her bed and looked over at her sister. Valerie was sleeping soundly with her mouth open slightly. Sam's gaze wandered across the dimply lit wall to a Wombles poster pinned over a shelf of seven leaning books. Next to that poster hung the framed picture of the ballerina, but it was hard to pick out the ballet dancer now, because of the low light level. Suddenly Sam saw something moving out of the corner of her eye. The thing was back – and this time it was twice as large. It was oozing into the room through the razor-thin gap at the top of the bedroom door, and this time the dark shape formed into a three-dimensional hand with freakishly long fingers, and it 'walked' along the wall on those fingers, like some surreal overgrown spider.

Samantha's breathing became rapid and shallow and she could feel her heart pounding in her chest. She felt weak and helpless and was frightened that she was going to faint. Then something inexplicable took place. The picture of the ballerina facing her started to light up, as if a small bulb had been switched on behind its canvas, and revealed the dancer as a gleaming silver figure. The faint sweet strains of the 'Dance of the Sugar Plum Fairy' filled the room, and the ballerina began to twirl about with a tread so light that she looked as if she could walk on flowers without harming the petals. She turned slowly and floated on the tip of her toe, and then gyrated faster and faster as the music grew in intensity.

Samantha felt herself becoming hypnotised by the enchanting spectacle, and her fear of the shadow-like hand gradually diminished. The hand then started to crawl back towards the bedroom door, and then to slowly retreat into the horizontal gap, stretching itself into a wafer-thin form in order to be able to do so. Yet it seemed to have difficulty in leaving the way it had come.

At this point Valerie woke up, thinking that Sam had turned a transistor radio on, and she moaned, "Turn it off, Sam, for goodness sake," and then yawned and opened her eyes. She blinked and saw the black spidery hand trying to squeeze through the narrow gap, and she let out a yelp and clasped her hands to her mouth. Then she noticed the silvery glow radiating from the picture and the ballerina dancing so gracefully within its frame.

Sam suddenly experienced something that felt like an implanted suggestion popping into her mind. She acted on this impulse from who knows where and reached under her bed for the electric torch. This was no ordinary torch, but one which could shine a rainbow of colours by turning a thumb wheel which slid coloured discs of cellophane over the bulb. She selected a rosy pink light and aimed the torch-beam at the hand. Its fingers began to wriggle violently and it lost its tenuous grip and fell to the floor.

"What is it?" screamed Valerie, kneeling now at the end of her bed, and staring in horror at the giant black spidery thing.

Sam got out of bed and walked over to the five-fingered creature writhing on the floor and shone the torch beam at it again, this time selecting an amber light. The gross black disembodied hand bubbled and emitted cheeps that sounded like a wounded sparrow. Valerie stepped over it and ran over to her sister – past the glowing picture of the ballerina – and attempted to drag her to safety, away from the unknown organism on the floor, but she could see it had now shrivelled to something resembling a wet black leaf. Sam seemed to be in some kind of trance, and Valerie laid her down on her own bed and hugged her reassuringly, as she shouted for her mother.

Mrs Armitage came rushing into the room and unknowingly stepped on the last vestiges of the thing that had terrorised her daughters for the last two nights. Only when Valerie pointed out that she had stepped on it, did Janet look, and she kicked off her slippers and screamed. She switched on the light, and as she did so, both girls could now see that the ballerina's picture had returned to normal. The enigmatic dancer had adopted her usual static pose once again.

After those two eventful nights, there were no further middle of the night disturbances in that house in Norris Green. Mr Armitage had no reason to question what his daughters and wife had told him. He conjectured that something good and something evil were once contained in that attic, and they had each kept the other in check. However, the evil thing had been accidentally released when the paraphernalia was removed from the attic, and was then at liberty to terrorise the family.

What the significance of the ballerina was in that painting and who she was, was never determined. Directories and Census records were trawled through in an attempt to find a ballet dancer who had lived at the house in the past, but without any success whatsoever. John and Janet researched the history of the house and the site on which it stood, as far back as the 1840s, but found nothing which could throw any light on the strange goings on in their home that November in 1975. The unsigned oil painting of the ballerina has even been scrutinised by an art expert, but he was unable to discover who had painted the dancer, although he believed the style suggested it had been executed in the 1880s, perhaps in France.

CABBIE'S NIGHTMARE

Mike, a Huyton taxi-driver remembers the exact date, time and place when this strange incident happened: Friday, 13 August 2004, just after 1 o'clock in the morning. He had just dropped off a passenger and was driving down Queen's Drive, when he spotted a woman of about sixty years of age, standing on the kerb in front of Holly Lodge Girls' College. She raised her arm to signal him to stop and Mike pulled over and the woman climbed into his vehicle.

"Lower House Lane," she said, and slammed the passenger door very hard behind her as she sat down.

Mike drove off and glanced in his rear-view mirror. The woman looked just like his mother; curly tightly-permed hair, spectacles, and a beige mackintosh. He attempted to make light conversation with her, saying, "I think we're in for some rain later."

To which his passenger replied, "We're in for much more than that."

"Oh, how's that?' said Mike, turning up Muirhead Avenue.

"These are the Final Days!" roared the woman. "That's what!"

Mike was startled by both the tone of her voice and her ominous words. A cab-driver knows in the first few seconds what type of person his fare is; whether the passenger prefers to stay tight-lipped or talkative, is sociable or a psycho. Mike was already thinking that this lady most definitely belonged in the latter category.

"Final days of what?" Mike inquired innocently.

"The final days of the battle between God and the Devil!" the woman shouted loudly.

"Oh, is it really?" Mike said, and tutted. For once, his Scouse wit had failed him. What could he possibly say in reply to something so outlandish.

The woman took the challenge badly and unleashed a barrage of four-letter expletives and then called the cabby an idiot. Mike slowed down, deciding that he was not prepared to take this abuse off his passenger, even if she was of a mature age. He pulled over on Dwerryhouse Lane and turned round to confront the unbalanced woman. What he saw was completely unexpected. The woman was shaking violently with her arms outstretched and her head lolling about. Her hands were almost touching the two side windows. Blood was trickling from her forehead, and it also began to drip from her wrists, soaking the cuffs of her mackintosh. Without warning, the woman suddenly let out an ear-splitting scream, louder than anything Mike had ever heard coming from the mouth of a human being. It sounded as if her voice was being channelled through a thousand-watt concert amplifier, and Mike felt his eardrums painfully pop. Most taxis nowadays have microphones fitted inside the rear of the cab, so that the driver can hear his passengers' directions via an amplifier, but the woman's voice was so loud that it caused the chassis of the cab to shudder in the most alarming way. When she finally stopped screaming, she crumpled in a heap on to the floor of the taxi.

Mike jumped out of his cab and wrenched open the passenger door – only to find that the vehicle was now completely empty – yet he could still hear a moaning sound coming from inside. He turned on the inside lights and checked under the seats, and in every nook and cranny, but there was absolutely nothing there. The moaning gradually faded away, and Mike examined the floor of the taxi to see if there was any blood on the carpet – again there was nothing to be seen, not even the tiniest speck of blood.

Mike drove off feeling very shaken up, and slowly had to come to terms with the only disturbing explanation that fitted the facts: he had had a ghost in his cab. As he drove past West Derby Cemetery, on Lower House Lane – the destination the eerie woman had given after getting into the taxi – he heard another horrendous scream in the back of his cab. He braked hard, and turned to see something flit from the back of his cab and into the cemetery. It looked like some kind of white fluttering object, possibly a sheet of white cloth, but Mike could not be sure exactly what it was, because of the velocity at which it moved.

From what Mike has described to me of the events that happened to him that day, it seems as if the woman must have been a religious fanatic during her lifetime. The blood dripping from her wrists and forehead seems to suggest that she had suffered from the mysterious inflictions of a baffling but well-documented phenomenon known as stigmata. I presume that the body of the passenger who terrified Mike that night is buried in West Derby Cemetery. Yet just whose ghost hailed a taxi that night on the ominous date of Friday the thirteenth, remains a mystery.

SUMMON THE BESERKER

From the late 1990s up to 2005, a larger than life, yet modest, middle-aged man known only as O'Neil, was a fairly regular visitor to The Swan Inn on Wood Street. Without a doubt, he practised magic. Not the mechanical sleight-of-hand street-magic variety, but the type we associate with the great Merlin in that lost Arthurian age, though of a far lesser magnitude. He was conversant with spirits and was very scathing of show business mediums and charlatans, and he would only enlist the help of the dead when it was an absolute necessity, because he had learned at an early age that the true medium risks his sanity by knowing too much about his and everyone else's future.

O'Neil did not take drugs, but he was fond of his drink; perhaps it served to dull his keen but ultimately troublesome psychic senses. If you visited the Swan Inn during the time period to which I am referring, you would probably have seen O'Neil but wouldn't have given him a second glance. You would have seen a man with straggly mousy-grey hair in a scuffed leather biker's jacket and faded jeans, Doc Martens and a world-worn face, pulling on a roll-up of Golden Virginia tobacco. At heart, he was a very inoffensive man, but because he chose never to lie in life, he upset many people when he gave them straight answers, and this happened one December night at the Swan, in 2005.

Liverpool, being a maritime city, is prone to heavy fogs, and in November 2005 the mother of all fogs enshrouded the whole of the North West. Flights in and out of John Lennon Airport were cancelled because of it. It spread as far as Manchester and Blackpool and caused transport chaos and fatalities on the roads, and unlike the usual fogs, this one stuck around for days. When O'Neil came into the Swan Inn that night for his usual Guinness, and perhaps a short or two, wisps of the fog snaked in behind him. He took his place in his usual corner seat with his drink, and then in came his young friend, Harlan, talking about astrology and palm-reading. O'Neil laughed and remarked that around thirty million people in Britain followed the advice of "newspaper horoscope prophets" and that there must be some turmoil going on in the heavens when two football teams meet on the pitch, because we would have twenty-two star-signs in conflict, plus the referee and linesman's star-signs battling it out.

"Then what about palms?" Harlan asked O'Neil, studying his own young soft work-shy hands.

"Now there's an very interesting subject ..." O'Neil was saying, when there came sniggers from a neighbouring table.

Two huge bikers sat there, clad in black motorcycle leather jackets, black tee shirts, Kevlar-panelled jeans, Harley Davidson Interstate zip boots, and Nazi tattoos. There were both smirking at O'Neil.

O'Neil did his best to ignore them, and had just taken Harlan's palm in order to study it, when the bikers came over to the table and sat themselves down by the mystic and his young friend.

"Read our future, mate," ordered the tallest and broadest of the two trouble-causers, and he thrust out a rough-palmed hand and laughed, "if we have any future that is."

O'Neil looked at the biker's hand for a few moments, then with a serious voice asked, "Are you sure you want to know?"

"Don't give me that crap," said the biker, using his aggression to try and cover up his nervousness. "You can see nothing ... no one can ... and you're filling this lad's head here with rubbish. You're just a flaky old man. Admit it!"

The biker's associate giggled.

"Very well, I'll start with your past," said O'Neil, looking quite ruffled.

"Sure, go ahead!"

The outspoken biker shoved his palm right under O'Neil's nose. The Liverpool shaman took hold of that palm, placed it on the table, and bluntly said, "You've lost so many women over the years because you're a violent man. You hit women."

The biker blinked rapidly and said nothing but it was obvious to the two onlookers that O'Neil had touched a delicate nerve.

"Oh, come on, who hasn't struck a woman?" said the biker, but behind the bravado and the smile his eyes looked distressed.

"And you stole from your mother on her deathbed."

After dropping this bombshell, O'Neil looked up from the palm to the biker's face with uncharacteristic contempt. Harlan had never seen such a look of disgust in his friend's face before.

The biker withdrew his palm and felt for the hunting knife which he kept in a sheath sewn into the inside of his jacket. He let loose a string of shockingly obscene expletives, at which a gothic-looking woman entering the Swan Inn shouted over, "Hey, there's no need for that language!"

The other biker grabbed hold of his friend's hand and stopped him from pulling out the knife destined for O'Neil's heart. "Don't man!" he pleaded.

The once-sceptical hard-knock who had had his shameful past so publicly revealed by O'Neil's chiromancy, stood up and shrieked, "I'll be waiting out there for you!" He then threw the glass of Guinness in the mystic's face and swaggered out of the pub, repeating his threats.

Later that night, Harlan cagily ventured out into the fog – and soon spotted the burly biker waiting in a dark warehouse doorway, but there was no sign of his friend. Harlan rushed back into the pub and warned O'Neil to go to his home – wherever that was – via Hanover Street, but O'Neil somehow knew that the biker's friend would be waiting there; he could sense them both waiting.

"The other one has a machete, and he's used it before," was O'Neil's chilling remark.

"Then call the police. What are you waiting for?" Harlan urged his old friend.

"I'll call on a much higher authority to protect me, but it'll probably cause even more bloodshed," was O'Neil's mysterious response.

"What do you mean?" asked Harlan, intrigued but still worried.

"I need your help, Harlan," said O'Neil, rolling yet another cigarette. "We need to call him ..." he added.

"Call who for heaven's sake?" said Harlan, getting frustrated. "Stop talking in riddles. Can't you see this is really serious?"

"I need to call my guardian ... a berserker," said O'Neil, whilst calmly licking the Rizla paper and sealing his cigarette. Then he chillingly revealed how this guardian had, many years ago, knocked at his door in order to show him the severed head of a man who had raped the girl he loved.

Harlan went cold. He was speechless. He had never once had reason to doubt the incredible things his friend had told him, for it was a fact that O'Neil never lied – but surely he didn't have the power to conjure up one of the most feared warriors of history?

"Norse Occultism," said O'Neil, and went over to the female goth who had scolded the foul-mouthed biker, and asked to borrow her make-up mirror. At first she thought he was joking, but he pleaded for it and promised to return it very shortly. She delved into her handbag and located it, then handed it to him with a sarcastic lop-sided smile.

O'Neil took it back to the table and then rooted through his own pockets for his trusty Swiss Army knife. "I need blood," he quipped.

"Last orders," shouted the barman.

O'Neil inflicted a small wound on his thumb, and then squeezed a few droplets on to the mirror.

"Váli, God of revenge," he intoned. "By my own blood I beseech thee to dispatch my guardian in the reign of Nótt, Goddess of this night ..."

"Hey, mate, what're you doing to my mirror?" the gothic lady shouted over, drawing people's attention to the weird ritual. "That's not blood, is it?"

O'Neil ignored her question. His eyes bulged and his muscles tensed as he proceeded to speak in an unknown language, and he frothed slightly at the mouth. Harlan was visibly trembling, because he could literally feel the buzz of electrical tension in the air. Silence descended on the Swan Inn – all eyes were on O'Neil. Suddenly, he fainted and slumped forwards on to the table, scattering ashtrays and spilling drinks, which made people assume that he was drunk. The clientele supped the last of their drinks and started to leave, and as they did so O'Neil regained consciousness. The first thing he did was to look into Harlan's eyes and with great solemnity declare, "He's here. I saw him."

O'Neil and Harlan were the last customers to leave the pub. They stepped out into a literal void of ghostly all-enveloping fog. The lamps of Wood Street were greatly diffused like distant nebulae, and passers-by appeared as insubstantial as the faint shadows of ghosts and spectres.

All of a sudden, the muffled silence of the fog was pierced by echoing screams. Not just the screams of women, but of men too, and not the usual screams of high-jinks fuelled by drink and drugs, but screams from witnesses to some shocking horror. O'Neil froze in his tracks, and Harlan halted too and looked back at him. The disturbance was coming from the

Slater Street intersection. O'Neil beckoned Harlan to follow him down Colquitt Street, but as they sneaked along the street, close to a wall, they heard the thundering steps of something striding by, and Harlan glimpsed a tall stocky phantasm walking along. It was as pale as a watermark in the fog, yet he could clearly make out a pair of horns on the stranger's head! He also carried a sword and circular shield.

That was enough. Harlan dashed after O'Neil, and they walked and walked until they reached Chinatown. O'Neil advised his friend to go straight home, and Harlan reluctantly obeyed. He walked for miles through that unending fog until he finally reached his home on Hawarden Avenue, off Smithdown Road, where he told his older brother all about the night's strange events. His brother looked at him condescendingly and said it was time he grew up.

Out of curiosity, on the following morning, Harlan rode the Number 86 bus into town and inspected Wood Street, looking for evidence of the berserker. He found splashes of clotted blood near Concert Street, and streaks of blood on the kerb near Hanover Street. He also heard strange stories about the berserker from his friends in the Krazyhouse club. Moshers, skater-punks, metalheads and Goths told him that "a drugged-up psycho", dressed like a Viking, had almost slaughtered two bikers, but the victims had run for their lives and escaped. The accounts varied slightly, but Harlan knew the truth of the matter and kept quiet.

At around this time, I also heard about a severed index finger being found on Wood Street, but whether there was a connection with this story, I am not sure. As far as I know, the violent bikers never returned to the Swan Inn, and O'Neil is now believed to be living quietly in Wales.

A genuine practitioner of magic has a great knowledge of grimoires – a comprehensive collections of spells and invocations which can be used for enlisting the help of demons. The demon Agares, for example, is conjured up to cause earthquakes, amongst other things, and the demon Behemoth (mentioned in the Bible's *Book of Job*) is concerned with food, drink and feasting, while Astaroth, the Prince-demon of Hell, will truthfully answer any questions about people or events, past present or future.

I know many people who mock magical rites, yet will mutter "Bless you" when someone sneezes. The celebration of a twenty-first birthday, the blessing of the Christian Eucharist, or even the rite of passage known as barmitzvah – are all ceremonial observances – the performance of rites. Magical rituals are indistinguishable from many of the everyday things we do that seem, on the face of it, irrational. We throw a pinch of salt over our shoulder for good luck, cross our fingers in hope, avoid walking under ladders and so on. Call such things superstition, if you like, or are they a subconscious harking back to the days when the practice of magic was widespread?

MR MERRILOCKS

Between the years 1967 and 1977, at a house overlooking Whitley Gardens on Shaw Street, a sinister entity made a number of regular and terrifying appearances, and this entity, which was around three-feet in height, was seen by numerous members of the community, including a student doctor and a social worker.

The earliest sighting of the paranormal creature took place one summer evening in July 1967. Twelve-year-old Stephen had brought a group of similarly aged friends into the back parlour of his fifty-seven-year-old Auntie Gwen's home to play Subbuteo. By about 8 o'clock, most of Stephen's friends had gone home, and only his best friend, Will Jenkins, remained. The two boys enjoyed drawing, and so Stephen sneaked up to his Aunt Gwen's room and stole six or seven sheets of paper from the writing pad in her bureau and a few pencils, then nipped back downstairs to the back parlour – which he found to be empty!

Will Jenkins was not there, and on the floor, there was a trail of liquid that later proved to be urine. Jenkins had seen something so heart-stopping in that parlour, that it had caused him to wet his pants and dash straight out of the house. On the following day, Stephen went round to Will's home on Langsdale Street and asked him why he had run out of the back parlour the night before. Will was shaking like a leaf when he gave an answer. He said that a little scary-looking man, about three-feet tall, had come walking down the wall, and had chased him out of the house brandishing a long knife.

"You're a liar," Stephen told Will, but it was wishful thinking. He *hoped* his best friend was lying, but inwardly he knew that he was not.

"I'm not lying. I saw him and I'm not going to your auntie's house ever again," said Will, as he gulped back tears.

At this point the frightened boy's mother came to the door and told Stephen that Will couldn't play out because he had to get a bath. Stephen walked away dejectedly, and decided to go home to tell his mother about his friend's far-fetched story. She shook her head and laughed, but then her sister Gwen called and told her about the dreadful urine stain on the carpet in her back parlour. Only then did Stephen's mother realise that something strange must have happened. She forbade Stephen to go into that back parlour and then told Gwen about her son's incredible tale. Gwen dismissed it all as just childish nonsense, for she had seen nothing strange in the back parlour, or in any other room in the house for that matter, during the ten years she'd lived there.

Stephen was not convinced and became obsessed with trying to find the dwarf with the knife, and one day he stole the spare key to his Aunt Gwen's house, which was kept in an old coffee tin in one of the drawers of his mother's dresser. He sneaked into Gwen's house on an afternoon when she was out visiting a friend, and made a beeline for the back parlour. The boy was afraid yet exhilarated. He just had to see the thing that had scared Will with his own eyes, and his wish was to be granted.

The time was 3pm, and although it was a summer's afternoon outside, a strange gloom descended on the back-parlour as he very gingerly opened the door; it was as if the windows had suddenly become tinted. A rhythmic sound, caused by some kind of friction, could be heard in the room. Stephen stiffened, and then looked around. There was no one about, yet the noise persisted. He looked down, and then behind him, and still saw nothing. Then his nostrils detected an odd out-of-place aroma – the scent of cinnamon. Something wet appeared on Stephen's nose; a tiny droplet of clear liquid. Then he heard that grating sound again. He shuddered and looked up. A bizarre-looking little man in a medieval black garment with a brown hood, was dangling precariously from the arms of the old brass chandelier by his legs. He was grating his teeth in the most horrible way, and long strings of saliva were dripping down on to the petrified boy. The dwarf suddenly reached into his belt for a long knife, then dropped down head first towards Stephen. The boy reflexively stepped backwards, then turned and ran screaming for the door. He opened that door and slammed it shut behind him, pulling hard on the brass door-knob, in case the little monstrosity should try to open it from the inside.

The sound of the dwarf's knife rhythmically stabbing at the door gave Stephen palpitations. In order to escape, he decided that he would have to let go of the doorknob, then pelt down the hall to the vestibule door, and straight out of the house. The stabbing blade sounds stopped abruptly, and Stephen got ready to run, when he felt a sharp pain in his big toe. He looked down and to his horror saw the small blade thrusting to and fro through the gap under the back parlour door.

He turned and ran, and as he did so he heard the back parlour door being flung open behind him. Stephen was too scared to look back, but he could hear unearthly high-pitched laughter in the hallway, and knew his assailant was snapping at his heels. He reached the vestibule door, opened it, and slammed it behind him, and once again he heard the stabbing sounds of the dwarf's blade attacking the wood. The boy tried to open the front door, but someone was pulling the door away from him on the other side! He panicked and tried desperately to get out of the vestibule, but there was someone in the way.

It was Aunt Gwen. She had returned earlier than he had expected and she had been turning the key in the lock at the same time as he had been trying to open the door. He yelled for her to get out of the way, and as she recoiled in shock, her nephew flew down the three steps to the pavement and tripped over, skinning his palms and his kneecap. He picked himself up, looked back at his startled aunt, and ran off to his home on Netherfield Road without stopping to give her any kind of explanation.

When Stephen reached home he found his toes squelching about inside a bloody shoe. His mother washed the stabbed toe and took him to the Royal Hospital on Pembroke Place to have it checked out. The toe was merely grazed, but Stephen's mother was now prepared to take her son's story seriously, and she and her husband called at Gwen's house to put her in the picture. Gwen was as baffled as ever, and was only too happy to show them the back parlour. Everything looked completely innocuous and as it should be. There was certainly no evidence of any psychopathic midget. However, Stephen's parents also noticed the unaccountable aroma of cinnamon, and Gwen had to admit that it was strange, for she had never used that ingredient in her cookery. Even now, in adulthood, Stephen finds that the smell of cinnamon triggers a reaction in him; he immediately feels his heart racing and his hands become cold and sweaty.

Stephen refused to visit his aunt after that day, and six months after the encounter with the oddly-dressed bantam-weight knifeman, Gwen moved to Wales. The house was then inhabited by two sisters in their fifties named Joyce and Edna. Joyce, a widow, had a seven-year-old granddaughter called Elsie who often came to visit them on Sundays. One Sunday the child went missing, and could not be found anywhere. An hour elapsed and just when the police were about to be sent for, Elsie was found crying in the back parlour. Most of her beautiful red locks were missing. The child was incoherent, and hysterical, but when she later calmed down, she said that a little man named Mr Merrilocks had tied her up and put a gag in her mouth. He had then used a knife to roughly hack off her collar-length air.

The adults believed that a would-be child-snatcher must have broken into the house and called in the police, but they could find no trace of such a person having been in the house, and surmised that a young tearaway, who had somehow gained access to the back parlour, had been responsible. The strange story reached the ears of Stephen's father, and he in turn told his wife. Stephen's mother visited the house on Shaw Street and told Joyce and Edna about Stephen's encounter with the dwarf, and the sisters were so spooked by the tale, that they later moved.

100

The ghost's sinister reputation continued for a number of years, but the dwarf seems to have made himself scarce during that period – until January 1970, that is – when he was seen by a group of students who had just moved into the house. It has not yet been ascertained whether he was merely seen, or whether he attacked anyone during this period. I have received many emails and letters about Merrilocks, including a detailed sighting of the entity by twenty-five-year-old social worker Freda, who lived close to the house on Shaw Street in 1972.

Freda had lost the key to her front door one evening, and so went round to the back alleyway behind her home to gain access via the backyard door. As she walked along, she saw something she mistakenly identified as a dog at first. She squinted in the poorly-lit entry and saw that this dog had only two legs, and suddenly she recognised that the thing was actually a little man with a reddish brown hood on his head. The rest of his clothes were jet black. The dwarfish figure had stopped in the entry, and seemed to be rooting about in a neighbouring rubbish chute in the wall. It stopped and turned to look at Freda, and she could see that its beady eyes were now fixed on her.

She closed the yard door and darted across the yard to hammer on the kitchen door of her flat, but her boyfriend, Duncan, who was training to be a doctor, was not in the kitchen. Freda looked at the yard door and watched as it opened slightly. The long nose of the dwarf protruded from behind that door, and then the rest of its face came into view. It was grinding its teeth in a truly sinister way, and Freda felt her legs go weak at the knees. She made a fist and pounded on the kitchen window, and much to her relief, just at that moment Duncan came into the kitchen and heard his girlfriend's banging on the kitchen windows. He opened the kitchen door and found Freda standing there in a state of abject fear. She pointed to the thing peeping around the backyard door, and it ran off as Duncan bravely went after it. He clearly saw the weird-looking miniature prowler scurrying away down the dark entry.

The last sighting of Mr Merrilocks was in March 1977, when ten-year-old Martin Sharkey saw him walking down the wall in the back parlour of his home, apparently defying the laws of gravity. Having reached the floor, he threw his knife at the boy, and the blade hit him, but fortunately only glanced off his shoulder without penetrating the skin. The boy's father went into the parlour and saw nothing, even though the knife-throwing incident had taken place just seconds earlier. The boy made a detailed felt-tip sketch of the dwarf, depicting his black medieval garb with a brown hood, an extraordinary huge pair of 'fly away' eyebrows, and a ridiculously overlarge nose.

The Punch-like figure is exceedingly difficult to explain. What are we to make of the aroma of cinnamon that he gave off, his disproportionate physical features, and his medieval attire? Where did he come from? All questions which, by now, will probably never be answered, unless, of course, Mr Merrilocks comes out of retirement and decides to walk the Everton district again ...

WOOLTON'S WHISTLING GHOST

Many readers of my Local Mysteries column in the *Merseymart* and *Star* get in touch with me on a weekly basis and often provide me with fascinating information regarding intriguing local history tales, UFO sightings, and, of course, details of encounters with the supernatural. An email from a reader in October 2007 led to my investigation of the following puzzling story.

On Monday, 1 October 2007, at approximately 9pm, twenty-two-year-old Hayley was walking up Menlove Gardens East, in Allerton, on her way to a friend's house on Eldred Road. As she walked along the leaf-strewn pavement, her thoughts were about as far away as possible from the world of the paranormal. Yet as she passed Menlove Gardens North, she became aware of an ethereal faint whistling sound. She glanced around without stopping and out of the corner of her eye, she could see that someone was walking behind her, so she gradually quickened her pace. The whistling man seemed to speed up too, so Hayley surreptitiously delved into her handbag and took out her mobile phone, ready to call the police, for she felt that the man behind her was about to pounce at any moment. Suddenly, two girls aged about fifteen or sixteen, walking on the other side of the road, started screaming and stopped in their tracks. They were gazing directly at the man who had been walking so closely behind Hayley, with their hands to their shocked faces.

Hayley turned around to see what had caused this reaction in the girls, and saw to her horror that the man following her had no legs, and he looked as if he was floating several feet above the ground. The man had two hollow black sockets where his eyes were supposed to be, his face and hands were a deathly white, and he was still whistling as he floated inexorably towards Hayley. The teenaged girls turned and ran off down Woolton Road, and Hayley ran across the same road in the other direction towards Eldred Road. The ghostly pursuer apparently gave up the chase at the junction of Woolton Road and Menlove Gardens West, because Hayley looked back at that point, and after almost being hit by a car, she saw that the sinister legless apparition was now nowhere to be seen.

Not surprisingly, Hayley now refuses to go anywhere near Menlove Gardens North, South or West since that spine-chilling incident. As terrified as Hayley was, she was somewhat relieved to hear that the same ghost with no legs had been seen before in the areas of Allerton and Calderstones in the year 2000. I first received word of the curious ghost in 2001, at Radio Merseyside, and even staked out the Menlove Gardens area with two other ghost-hunters, but we saw nothing. Now, it seems, the whistling phantom of Woolton is up to his old tricks again. I have sifted through old documents and census records regarding this ghost, in an effort to discover who he was when he was alive, and why he has no legs. Some think he was a disgraced man of the cloth, whilst a medium who investigated the floating stalker a few years ago, has claimed that he is Frederick Garrod, a butler who lost his legs in the First World War.

LIVERPOOL'S LOST TREASURES

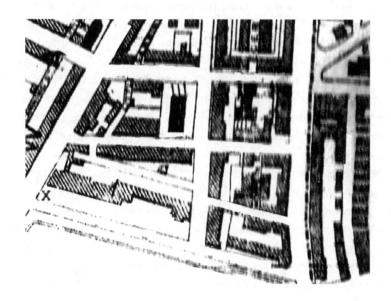

Many years ago, an elderly gentleman came to see me at Radio Merseyside and showed me a curious old gold coin. He told me that the coin was part of a fabulous treasure, buried centuries ago, now lying under soil "not far from Her Majesty's Prison Altcourse". He had studied all the references to this undiscovered treasure, which was purported to amount to the equivalent today of millions of pounds' worth of jewellery and gold, once the property of Ellen, heiress of Robert de Walton. The old man maintained that a separate treasure trove had been unearthed in a garden on Hawksmoor Road, in the 1970s, and that the finders had not declared it to the Queen, as the law required them to do. The Fazakerley Treasure, by comparison, was massive and was supposed to be hidden in three chests. However, despite knowing the general location of the treasure (close to the prison), treasure hunters were repeatedly turned away from the area by the authorities. I never saw that old man again after he told me about the treasure. Perhaps he has since died.

Liverpool has millions of pounds worth of treasure lying under its streets, much of it hidden in tunnels and secret passageways. For example, no one has yet managed to find the treasure trove stashed away in the days of Cromwell in the mile-and-a-quarter-long Everton Tunnel, which runs from Netherfield Road down to the docks. Some think the tunnel is linked to a separate one that runs from 'Prince Rupert's Hut' in Everton. It is known that in the 1900s, there was a place called the 'Newboys Home' in Everton Road, where destitute children could get supper and a bed for a penny a night. In the cellars of the home there was an entrance into the Everton Tunnel. Some of the boys went off exploring down the tunnel with home-made torches dipped in paraffin and managed to find gold rings and old coins.

When the authorities looked into the history of the tunnel, it was established that it had been excavated in the reign of King Charles I. Prince Rupert is said to have hidden the treasures he confiscated from the defeated Parliamentarians somewhere in the tunnel. Most of the treasure was in the form of gold ingots manufactured from melted down rings and jewellery. When Cromwell's men took Liverpool, they were unable to find these treasures, which were said to be sealed up in secret vaults inside the Everton Tunnel.

In May 1840, a group of Lancashire workmen digging an embankment up on the River Ribble, uncovered 8,600 items of treasure, including many silver and gold coins. They handed their findings over to Queen Victoria, but other people have chosen to keep treasure troves for themselves. In the 1980s, at the height of the metal-detector fad, two men obtained a strong signal from their metal detectors over a Formby sand-dune. They were seen to unearth a crumbling wooden chest filled with large gold coins. The men stashed the coins in holdalls and then drove off, leaving only the chest behind.

Greed for gold has even driven some criminals to raid the tombs of our Victorian dead. Many years ago there was a spate of grave robberies at St James's Cemetery. A considerable amount of jewellery was plundered from one vault, which brought nothing but bad luck to those who handled it. An onyx ring stolen from the tomb ended up on the finger of a woman named Joan, and she soon found that she could not remove it, no matter what she tried. From the moment she slid the ring on to her finger, she suffered terrible nightmares and the ghost of a woman in black followed her everywhere. The effect on her mind was devastating and Joan ended up in a lunatic asylum.

To date, no one has managed to find 'Holland's Gold' – a small crate containing perhaps as many as ten gold ingots, said to have been hidden by forty-nine-year-old Liscard merchant, Edgar Swinton Holland, shortly before his murder in 1896. Holland was the managing director of both the Santa Barbara and Pintangui gold mining companies, and had his office at Number 45 Drury Buildings, at Number 21 Water Street.

On Thursday, 29 October 1896, the wealthy bachelor (whose personal wealth was estimated at over £250,000) walked into his offices and entered the board room accompanied by his solicitor, a Mr Alsop, blissfully unaware that he had an appointment with death. As the two professional men entered the room, a beautiful thirty-two-year-old actress, dressed from head to toe in funereal black, rose from her seat and stared at the two men, quivering with emotion. Without taking a seat, and in a voice seething with suppressed anger and outrage, Edgar Swinton Holland addressed her, "Madam, although you have no moral or legal claims upon me, I am going to make provisions for you, but it will be under certain conditions. These conditions will have to be settled between your solicitor and mine ..."

This little speech had a terrible effect on the woman. She flew into a violent rage, and screamed, "I want no solicitors, or 'provisions' thank you very much! You promised to marry me and to leave me all your property, to compensate for all my losses and all the wrongs you have done me!"

With a slow intake of breath, Mr Holland again addressed the woman, smugly rejecting her claim, "Madam, I never promised to marry you. I never wronged you. I always treated you with the utmost kindness," he seethed, with ill-concealed contempt. He looked at the actress with disgust, as if she were some insect, or vermin, which must be got rid of.

The wronged woman, Catherine Kemspshall, retorted with, "You hound! You beast! How could you?" and as she spoke she reached under her cloak into a pocket in her jacket and produced a revolver. She emptied four of its chambers in quick succession, as she shot Edgar Swinton Holland at point-blank range. Mr Alsop, the solicitor, sprang to his feet, knocked the smoking revolver from Catherine Kempshall's hand

and pinioned her arms behind her back. Holland somehow managed to drag himself to his feet, groaning horribly and with blood gushing from the wounds in his chest, thigh and left wrist. He staggered across the floor to the woman who had fired at him and with his life slowly ebbing away, he gently placed his trembling hands on her shoulders, and tried to whisper something to her, but instead collapsed on to the floor.

A few days later, Edgar Swinton Holland died.

Catherine Kempshall was tried for murder in March 1897. Trying to plead insanity, her defence lawyers argued that she was suffering from a persecution mania, and also revealed that her aunt had died in a mental institution, but the actress cried out from the dock, "I am not mad at all! I am quite sane!" and on another occasion she told the jury: "I would much rather you sentence me to death. I do not want a reprieve; I do not want my life."

Catherine Kempshall was found guilty by the court and sentenced to hang, and as the black-capped judge intoned, "And may the Lord have mercy on your soul," she answered, "And He will!"

Despite the jury's verdict, Catherine had the sympathy of the general public and a petition was signed by 17,796 people – including relatives of Mr Holland – begging for clemency. One unfortunate individual who loudly and publicly proclaimed that the actress should be hanged, was almost battered to death by angry women who struck him with their umbrellas on Dale Street. A seventy-year-old American lady living in Liverpool even walked the streets of the city to personally collect seven hundred signatures.

On the day before Kempshall was due to hang at Walton Gaol, the Home Secretary acted on the weight of public opinion in the form of the petition, and had the prisoner removed to Broadmoor Criminal Lunatic Asylum. Catherine Kempshall spent fifty-six years within the walls of that grim institution, and it has to be assumed that they were not happy years, incarcerated as she was with those who had committed some of the most abominable crimes. She died, aged eighty-eight, in 1953.

For many years, the ghost of Edgar Swinton Holland is said to have been seen gazing fixedly down at a garden in Gambier Terrace, and some think the sad-looking spectre is gazing at the spot where he was supposed to have buried a crate of gold ingots. Why he buried the gold, and why he chose that particular location, is anybody's guess.

'OLIVE OYL'

O ne evening, in February 1937, twenty-two-year-old shy office clerk, Anthony Parl, set off for the Rialto Ballroom, which once stood on the corner of Upper Parliament Street and Stanhope Street. Parl was particularly looking forward to the St Valentine's Gala Night at the ballroom, because he had just started dating a new girlfriend, whom he had arranged to meet in the Rialto foyer. He walked along with a spring in his step, checking his hair and appearance in every shop window as he passed by. However, when he arrived at the ballroom there was no sign of Ivy. Never mind, that was a lady's prerogative. He waited for over an hour, during which time his mood changed from one of pleasant expectation to humiliation and despair, as he watched all the other happy couples entering the dance hall. He had to face it – Ivy, his girlfriend of six days, had stood him up.

Feeling crushed and dejected, Parl eventually sidled away from the Rialto foyer at 8.45pm and embarked on a heartbroken journey to a nearby tram stop. All he wanted to do was go home and wallow in his phonographic records about lost love. He was trudging along in this kind of melancholic mood, when he noticed a thin, sad-looking girl walking up Selborne Street. She looked about eighteen, and had her head bowed as she strolled along. Hardly believing that he was doing it, Anthony Parl crossed the road and found himself greeting the lonely-looking teenager. "Good evening, Miss," he said. The girl hesitated for a moment, lifted her pale face to him and tried to force a smile, but her lips barely moved and her two huge dark eyes were filled with pain and sadness. She walked on a while, but Anthony cried, "Wait!" which was so out of character for someone as bashful as himself. The girl waited. She stopped in her tracks, and Anthony spoke again, "Er, sorry for shouting like that … erm would you like to go to a dance with me?"

The girl shook her head without a word, but smiled faintly. She turned and continued down the street in the direction of the Synagogue, and Anthony felt an urge to follow her. "Would you like a cigarette?" he muttered, reaching for a packet in his coat pocket, but the girl's pace increased. The persistent clerk tailed her all the way to the Rialto, where the teenager stopped and waited at the entrance. Anthony took a drag of his cigarette and leaned against a nearby pillar, as he regarded the plain-faced yet beguiling girl. She stood there, alone, as people poured past her into the most popular dance venue in Liverpool.

By 9.15pm, she was still standing there alone, so Anthony decided to pluck up the courage to try and talk her into joining him in the ballroom – and to his utter amazement, the girl nodded her assent. Anthony eagerly bought the two two-shillings-and-sixpence tickets for the gala dance, and went inside with the girl, who gave her name as Olive.

During the course of the evening, Olive revealed that she had been stood-up by her boyfriend of three months, Edward. Anthony tried his utmost to cheer her up that evening. They danced all night, but hardly drank; all they wanted to do was dance. After the gala ended, at two in the morning, Anthony begged Olive to see him again, but the girl said she couldn't, and suddenly became tearful. Anthony took her in his arms and kissed her, and found her lips to be ice cold. He escorted her part of the way home, but when they reached Boswell Street, Olive insisted on making the rest of the journey alone, saying that she only lived a stone's throw away. Her father would be waiting for her and he would be furious at her staying out so late. Anthony kissed Olive again and said goodbye and sadly watched her walk off – and out of his life – but then, fearing for her safety at that hour of the night, decided to follow her at a distance. He reckoned that Olive didn't want him to see where she lived, because she didn't want to see him again, which hurt him deeply, because he was already so in love with the girl.

He watched her turn up Hartington Road, and then on to Smithdown Road – towards the gates of a cemetery! Olive walked straight through the closed gates, and as Anthony stood there, shocked and bewildered, he noticed a man walking from the pitch-blackness of the vast graveyard and approaching her. This man began to shout at the girl for being so late, and as he scolded her, they both faded away.

It seems 'Olive Oyl', as the ghost was nicknamed by those who knew about her, was some carnate restless spirit of a girl who was knocked down and killed on her way to a date at the Rialto in the late 1920, or early 1930s. Her broken-hearted father died soon afterwards and both are buried in Toxteth Park Cemetery.

MR TIXY

In 1996, Danny, a fifteen-year-old Croxteth teenager, was strumming the chords to a song by the Liverpool band Cast, called 'Walk Away'. That song had been his ex-girlfriend's favourite the year before when he had first started dating her, and now she had left him and was with someone else. Hot stinging tears streamed down Danny's cheeks, as he strummed the song and looked out of the window at the night falling on the fields beyond Croxteth Brook. Danny's mother came into his room, and upon finding him upset, sat down and told him that he must try and get over the loss of his girlfriend Keeley. "There're plenty more fish in the sea, lad," were his mother's well-intentioned but somewhat insensitive words. Platitudes are never enough at times of crisis, but, on the other hand, it is often difficult for mothers and sons to talk about emotional issues. Danny was so heartbroken that he even contemplated suicide that night, and with that depressing notion uppermost in his mind, he lay down on his bed and somehow fell fast asleep.

"Danny! Get up!" said a voice in the room.

Danny woke up with a start and for a moment imagined that it was his father calling him, but instead the truth was much stranger. The teenager squinted into the darkness and saw something sitting on his inside window ledge. It looked like a small child at first, but then Danny switched on his nightlight and tried to make sense of what his eyes were telling him. The diminutive person on the ledge was someone he had not seen for about ten years – Mr Tixy – his elf-like childhood friend. Danny was not into drugs and didn't even drink or smoke, so there was no doubt in his mind that the thing sitting on his window sill was not some hallucination.

"Long time no see," said Mr Tixy, in a casual friendly manner.

Danny sat up slowly in his bed and thought about shouting to his mum and dad, but tried to calm himself down instead. As his eyes adjusted to the half-light, he could see the little man quite clearly. He was about three feet tall, and wore a green shirt, pointed indigo cap, purple tights with pointed shoes, and sported a thick black beard around his corpulent rosy-cheeked face. Yes, it was definitely Mr Tixy, the little companion who would sit on his bed when he was five years of age and tell him countless stories. The adults had dismissed him as an imaginary friend, and had almost convinced Danny that he was nothing more than make-believe, but Danny had known better. It was 3am by the bedside clock, and behind Mr Tixy, the stars were twinkling through the window.

"Why did you leave me?" Danny asked, with a lump in his throat, remembering all those nights when he had cried as a child, because his little pal had abandoned him.

"Oh, I had things to do," said the Mr Tixy, rather guiltily, "and I lose track of time because a week where I come from is a year over here."

"Where *do* you come from, by the way?" Danny, asked, eager to know.

Mr Tixy refused to be precise but hinted that there was a place beyond the brook, just past the M57 motorway, where an undiscovered world existed. He then told the teenager why he had come back to see him after all this time – to try and cheer him up and put all thoughts of suicide out of his mind.

"Keeley will come back to you in the summer, Danny. Don't ever think of killing yourself – life will do that for you in the end anyway. See you around."

And in the blink of an eye, Mr Tixy was no longer there. No one was prepared to believe what Danny had seen that night, putting the whole experience down to his depressed state of mind. But two strange things happened later that year which made them all think again.

In the summer, Keeley fell in love with Danny all over again, and today they are happily married. That summer, when the reunion took place, Danny and Keeley were walking hand in hand through Croxteth Hall Country Park, when a couple passed with their three-year-old son. As the child passed, he pointed to an expanse of green lawn devoid of people and exclaimed: "Look! There's Tixy!" in a clear voice. The little boy's parents didn't even look to see what the excited child was looking at, but had they looked, they would almost certainly have seen nothing with their educated, sceptical eyes anyway. On this occasion, Danny saw nothing either, but knew that in a bygone golden age, when he was younger and more innocent, he too had seen things which the dullard adults had not. Danny walked on and smiled at the little boy. He realised that all adults are just children who have lost faith in the magical world that exists alongside our own one.

THE SWEETING STREET GHOST

The Sweeting Street Ghost is the spectre of a man in a tricorn (three-pointed) hat, with blood streaming from his empty eye sockets, as he staggers about with his hands outstretched along Sweeting Street, one of the oldest streets in the city centre. The L-shaped street was originally named Elbow Lane, but was subsequently named Sweeting Street, after the Alderman Sweeting, who was Lord Mayor in 1698. There have been several sightings of the ghost on Sweeting Street over the years, and most of these reports mention the particularly gory detail of the blood streaming from the apparition's eyes. Some witnesses to this mysterious spectre have stood their ground long enough to notice that the bloody eyes are the result of an arrow in each of the ghost's eyeballs.

A local historian, who wishes to remain anonymous, tells me that he came face to face with the Sweeting Street ghost one night in 1979, at around 11.15pm, on his way home from the pub. The historian was recovering from tonsillitis at the time, and, as he was taking antibiotics, he had not been drinking alcohol. As he passed Sweeting Street, he saw the vague outline of a man feeling the wall as he walked along, as if he was either blind, or unsteady on his feet through drink. As the man was groaning, as if in pain, the historian shouted to him, "Are you okay there?" and as the figure neared a lamp-light, the historian could see that he was dressed in clothes from the eighteenth century. An arrow protruded from each of the man's eyes, and blood was streaming from the sockets down the cheeks. The local history lecturer was struck by the fact that there was a faint glow, an aura, around the man. The realisation that he had come face to face with a ghost, struck him like a thunderbolt and he took to his heels and ran.

In April 2007, the ghost was seen by two men attempting to hail a taxi on Dale Street one night at 10.30pm. At first, they thought they were looking at someone in fancy dress, but then they too saw the blood streaming from the outlandish-looking man's eyes (but not the arrows oddly) and they were only too glad when a taxi stopped to take them away from something which was outside their normal experience, and which frightened them in a way that nothing else ever had.

A medium has been brought to Sweeting Street on two occasions, and she ascertains, rather curiously, that the man was a spy for the French, and had plans to help French soldiers invade Liverpool. His treachery was discovered and he was therefore punished accordingly in Sweeting Street, by means of a strange torture ritual. Two men skilled in archery fired arrows into his eyes and after the man – named 'Sprool', or 'Sproule', had almost bled to death, he was then run through with a sword, and buried nearby in an unmarked traitor's grave. The medium believes that the whole affair was hushed up, because the traitor was in the pay of a famous Liverpool family of the time.

On the evening of Saturday 25 February, 1797, a message, carried by an express rider, reached Liverpool. French vessels of war had landed at Fishguard in Wales, carrying a large body of troops, and had afterwards put to sea again. On the next morning the Lord Mayor of Liverpool called an emergency meeting, as there was a rumour going around that the town was in imminent danger of being invaded by the French. It would be the greatest invasion since the Norman Conquest of 1066, and some believed that the French would enlist the help of the United Irishmen. Napoleon was busy conquering central Europe at this time, and the newly-formed French government – The Directory – had formulated a plan to invade England. Fortunately, the invasion never happened and the French attempt at invading England through the back door of Wales was a complete disaster. The brave women of Fishguard dressed in scarlet tunics and tall black felt hats, and the French troops imagined they were looking at the fearsome British troops – and so they fled!

It is within reason to assume that Liverpool, being a major port at the time, harboured its fair share of French spies and collaborators, and so, perhaps the medium is right about the Sweeting Street ghost; maybe he is the shade of a French agent, or some Quisling from the eighteenth century.

THE CHALLENGE

On 1 July 2007, an historic new law, which would affect the health and safety of everyone in the country, was introduced into England: smoking was to be banned in all indoor public places. Smokers are now legally obliged to step outside of the pub, restaurant, or club to indulge in their habit, and the same goes for the workplace, whether you are a doctor, a barrister, a shop-worker, a librarian, or even a security guard.

In August 2007, two security guards from two neighbouring stores on Liverpool's Church Street, left the premises they had been patrolling and met in a disused doorway outside to have a lunch-break smoke. The guards, Mark and Ben, were aged twenty-four and forty-two respectively, and always enjoyed a little chat as they smoked their cigarettes in the doorway, watching the crowds of shoppers strolling by.

On this particular rainy August day, Mark and Ben talked about football – always their first topic of conversation – then about iPods, and then food. Ben was bemoaning the fact that he was on a diet, but Mark boasted that he was one of those lucky people who could eat and eat and never ever put on any weight. He always felt hungry too, and that, bragged the young guard, was the sign of true fitness. Then, for some reason, Mark mentioned a horror film that he had watched the night before and so the subject of the paranormal came up. Mark said he didn't believe in ghosts, but Ben said he wasn't sure, as he had witnessed some very strange things over the years.

"Oh, yeah! Such as?" Mark queried sceptically, exhaling cigarette smoke into the rain-raked air.

Ben thought for a while, then said, "Well, there's a house in Kensington, on Jubilee Drive, and no one stays there long. It's boarded-up now, and it's got a really bad reputation."

"And?" Mark said nonchalantly.

"I lived in that house as a kid for nearly a year, and I saw something there," Ben seemed lost in his reminiscenses, his eyes screwed up anxiously. "To this day I don't know what I saw. It's as if I blocked it out.

It gave me a fit, I was so scared, and when I woke up I couldn't remember a thing, but I had nightmares about it for years."

"Is that it?" Mark asked, flicking his cigarette stump twenty feet through the air. "You saw *something*!"

"Yeah that's it," said Ben, annoyed at the macho attitude Mark adopted whenever he thought he could put somebody on the spot. He decided to dare him to something, to challenge his infuriating bogus machismo.

"Okay then, if you're so hard, how about spending a few nights in the place?"

"What place?" Mark asked, and gazed at his watch.

Ben's patience was wearing thin. "The house on Jubilee, you idiot."

Mark smirked and shook his head disparagingly, as if his friend was talking nonsense.

"It's okay if you're too scared," Ben said, enjoying seeing his friend squirm for a change.

"Me? I'm not scared of anything, mate," Mark replied in a raised voice, startling passing shoppers.

"Okay, you're going to have to prove that," Ben said, and he dropped his cigarette and twisted his sole on it.

Mark spat at the floor.

The following Saturday night at 9.45pm, Mark was driven to Jubilee Drive by Ben. The young guard carried a huge holdall crammed with an Army sleeping bag, two day's worth of food and drink, a MagLite torch, some candles, and a book. The two guards had both had military training, and found it easy enough to scale the backyard wall of the derelict house without being seen and then break in. Once in the house, Mark and Ben did a quick reconnaisance of the place and soon realised that it had a rodent problem. Rain had seeped into the carpet in the parlour, giving the room a disgusting fungal aroma, so Mark decided to camp in one of the three upstairs bedrooms.

The two men both drank a can of lager, then Ben said he would be back on Monday morning to check on him. The terms of the wager were that he must stay there, on his own, without any communication with the outside world, for the entire weekend. If Mark was still there on Monday morning, Ben would give him two hundred pounds.

"No problem," said Mark. "You'd better go and find a cash machine – you'll definitely be needing it."

That Saturday night, just minutes after Ben had driven away, Mark thought he saw something out the corner of his eye. It was nothing more than a small shadow, but he wasn't quite sure if it had merely been a passing car's headlights shining through the gaps in the boarded-up bay window. For company, he immediately switched on the radio, and turned the volume down low. He then unfurled a rubber ground sheet and laid his sleeping bag on top of it. He left his torch on as he lit two candles, and already he felt as if he was not alone. Mark was a one-hundred-per-cent sceptic, yet he felt as if unseen eyes were upon him, so he tried to avoid thinking about the supernatural. He went on a tour of the deserted run-down house, sweeping the beam of his torch into draughty rooms with tattered curtains and mouldy walls, whilst wishing the night away. It was still only ten o'clock. After his tour of inspection, he went back into the room where the candles burned reassuringly, and listened to the radio for a while. Through a gap in the boards on the window, he could see a full moon lighting up the sky, and the sight of it gave him the jitters for some reason. When Mark was a child, a school-friend had once told him that there were more murders and violent crimes committed on the night of the full moon, than on any other night, and that 'fact' had stuck with him ever since.

After little more than an hour inside the creepy house, the security guard decided to cheat. Even though he was not supposed to talk to anyone, he dialled his girlfriend's number on his mobile and chatted to her for almost half an hour, after which, he felt a lot more confident. She had wanted him to take her out that Saturday night, but he had accepted Ben's wager instead.

"Don't worry, babe. When I collect this pile of dosh on Monday, I'll give you the night out of your life."

Nevertheless, he couldn't help wondering what Ben could possibly have seen when he was a kid to leave him traumatised with memory loss.

"Brrr brr. Brrr brr." The sound of his mobile phone reverberated eerily around the empty house, as a text message came through for him at 11.25pm. It was from Ben, and said, "Your gf told me you talked with her. Don't be a coward, go it alone or not at all."

Mark swore at the message and deleted it as soon as he had read it. He lay down on his sleeping bag for a while, but didn't feel in the least bit tired. On the contrary, he had never felt more alert; all his senses were primed, waiting for something to happen. He was like a coiled spring.

At one o'clock in the morning he shot up as a terrible cacophony started up outside his window in the back alleyway. A number of cats had begun meowing simultaneously, and it sounded like an orchestra of scalded felines. The sound had a horrible unearthly ring to it. Mark was trying to rationalise the awful din, when he suddenly noticed something, and his skin tingled all over, as goose pimples rose on his flesh.

There was no doubt about it, the cats were definitely calling out his name: "M-a-a-a-rk ... M-a-a-a-rk"

Mark tried to convince himself that it was just his imagination and turned the radio volume up to block out the squealing cats, then opened a packet of Hula Hoops, and devoured them. He craved something more substantial to eat, and so he took the prawn and mayonnaise sandwiches which his girlfriend had made for him out of the holdall and eagerly unwrapped them. They were scoffed within minutes. There were two thermos flasks in the holdall, one containing chicken soup and the other containing black coffee. The soup was drunk in no time and still Mark felt unsatisfied. He then delved about in the holdall for the bars of chocolate that were supposed to last for the next forty-eight hours, and he ate most of them in one go, one after the other. The act of eating in some way took his mind off his situation, but he couldn't eat all night, so eventually he tried to settle back down on top of his sleeping bag.

At almost three o'clock in the morning, Mark heard footsteps. They were so loud it was obvious that someone solid was coming up the stairs. He instantly imagined that someone on Jubilee Drive had phoned the police, after seeing his candles burning through the gaps in the boards on the windows. He stood up, ready to face them, struggling to get a story straight to explain his presence in the empty house.

The heavy footfalls reached the door of his room and Mark braced himself. He aimed the torch nervously at the door, expecting a policeman to enter, but instead, a man in black came into the room. Where his face should have been, there was a jagged hole, and inside that hole, illuminated by the MagLite torch, a nest of large over-fed maggots squirmed in a glistening mass, as the stranger's tongue wormed about. He made deep guttural sounds as he attempted to speak, and a strong stench of decomposing flesh filled the room. Mark screamed, and then vomited. He threw his radio at the faceless ghoul, and as it bounced off its head, bloated maggots plopped out of the opening. Mark doubled up and vomited again, and felt agonising cramps in his stomach. After he had stopped retching, he looked up, and saw that the grotesque man had vanished.

Then he felt something long and wet dangling from his mouth. Mark felt the thing hanging from his lips, and when he tried to touch it, it squirmed in his hand. Its head felt as if it had pincers on it, and suddenly, with utter dread, Mark remembered his biology lessons at school and the tall glass jar in the science lab where the impossibly long anaemic tapeworm was suspended in formaldehyde. His hunch was right, it was a tape worm – a parasite that can live in the human gut and grow to enormous lengths. The largest ones can grow up to fifty-nine feet in length, and in Mark's case, the worm was about twenty feet long and as narrow as a pencil. It was removed from him in hospital whilst he was unsedated and fully conscious. The tape worm had grown inside his body from an egg that had been lying dormant in raw fish from a sushi dish. Had he not vomited that night, when he was confronted by the gross carnate apparition of the man with no face in that house, he may never have known that he was carrying around one of nature's most efficient parasites. The guard had never suspected for one minute that his over-keen appetite and slim build were symptoms of sharing his food with the voracious tape worm.

Just whose ghost haunts that house on Jubilee Drive is unknown, but I have heard about it a few times before. Some say the ghost is the earthbound spirit of a vagrant who fell down the stairs whilst squatting in the house and sustained a floating fracture of the face. His corpse had been rotting away unbeknown to anyone, until neighbours started noticing an unbearable stench and alerted the police. That is just hearsay, and no one seems to know why that repulsive maggot-infested ghoul continues to haunt that empty house.

As for Mark and Ben; the latter did not have to part with his hard-earned cash and had his fears about the house on Jubilee drive confirmed, and Mark is now far less cocky and his appetite has returned to normal. But he will not forget that night in the haunted house in a hurry, and will be far less ready to scoff at anything supernatural in the future.

THE HALLOWEEN VISITOR

In October 2006, twenty-seven-year-old Kelly from Great Sutton, was invited to a Halloween fancy dress party in Liverpool, organised by her cousin, Claire. The party, which was held at a house on Deysbrook Lane, West Derby, a mere stone's throw from Liverpool Football Club's training ground, went on into the early hours of 1 November. By one o'clock in the morning, the over-consumption of vodka had gone to Kelly's head, and she felt nauseous, so her cousin Claire took her upstairs and put her in the spare bedroom, then closed the door after her.

Kelly lay on the bed and moaned quietly to herself as she felt the room slowly spinning. The only light in the room was the faint golden illumination provided by a sodium streetlamp outside somewhere. Kelly could hear the faint strains of the party music and the nonsensical jumble of chatter from the people downstairs, and she longed to be back home with Tabitha, her lovely little six-year-old daughter in Great Sutton. The child was staying with her grandparents in Little Stanney, and would no doubt be missing her mum as much as she was missing her.

Kelly closed her eyes to try and stop the nausea and thought of her daughter as she drifted off into a sleep that was haunted by strange jumbled images and echoing sounds. She felt a man's hand stroking her face, and then she found herself reclining on a luxurious king-sized four-poster bed in a large elaborately-decorated bedroom. Is this a dream? Kelly wondered. It didn't seem real, yet it didn't feel like a dream either. The Halloween party was now only a vague memory. It was still night-time though, and, peeping between the heavy satin drapes surrounding the bed, she could see a full moon shining its thin silvery light through the exceedingly tall windows.

Kelly decided to get off the bed and noticed that she was wearing a long old-fashioned nightgown, whose oyster-coloured silken folds reflected the moonlight. She left the bedroom and found herself in a long red-carpeted galleried landing, and here she met a man in his late twenties with long hair, a twirled-up moustache, and dressed in the attire of a cavalier from the days of Cromwell. He seized Kelly and kissed her passionately on the lips, then scooped her up and carried her back to the bedroom and roughly laid her on the four-poster. The man then produced a small bottle, uncorked it, and ordered Kelly to drink from it. She told him she didn't want to but the man put the bottle to her lips and forced her to drink the vile fluid. She spat some of it out but couldn't stop herself from swallowing a small quantity of the liquid. The man then gazed into her face with an evil stare and triumphantly declared that she had drunk rum containing the ashes of her lover's heart!

Kelly screamed, and slapped the man's face, but he retaliated by slapping her back even harder.

Kelly woke up in a cold sweat, and realising that the dream had been nothing more than a very realistic nightmare, she sighed with relief, then squinted at the clock. It was almost two in the morning. She had only been asleep for fifty-five minutes, although it felt like much longer. Her head spinning, she got up, and went to the toilet to be sick. As she was returning to the bedroom, promising herself that she would never again touch another drop of alcohol, her friend Lisa came upstairs and helped her across the landing. "Come on, you poor thing. Your face looks green. No more vodka for you, young lady!"

"Too right, Lisa. Never again!"

As Lisa helped Kelly into the bedroom, she glanced around and asked, "Where is he?"

"Where's who?" asked Kelly, aching to lie down again to stop the room from spinning round.

"That musketeer fellow," Lisa said, and gave a chilling explanation.

Apparently, fifteen minutes before, she and Claire had tiptoed into the bedroom to check that Kelly was okay, and had found a long-haired man dressed like one of the Three Musketeers, sitting on the bed, holding her hand. The two girls had assumed he was an admirer of hers in fancy dress, as she was talking to the man.

"I was talking to no one, I've been asleep," mumbled Kelly, suddenly feeling much more sober. She thought Lisa was pulling her leg, at first, but when she checked with Claire, she vindicated the story.

Kelly was so upset by the story of the weird bedside stranger, that she phoned her father in the middle of the night and begged him to drive to

Liverpool to pick her up. Even when she was safely back at home in Great Sutton, Kelly slept uneasily, and wondered why she had been haunted by the sinister 'cavalier'.

I may be wrong, but the spooky incident involving Kelly took place quite close to Croxteth Hall, the former country estate and ancestral home of the Molyneux family and the Earls of Sefton. Perhaps some restless ghost of a past earl from the seventeenth century paid Kelly a visit that Halloween night and re-enacted some bygone and long-forgotten act of skulduggery. Like so many of these supernatural happenings, we can only hope that the answer to the mystery will be revealed one day.

OTHER TITLES BY TOM SLEMEN

HAUNTED LIVERPOOL 1	Tom Slemen	£5.99
HAUNTED LIVERPOOL 2	Tom Slemen	£5.99
HAUNTED LIVERPOOL 3	Tom Slemen	£5.99
HAUNTED LIVERPOOL 4	Tom Slemen	£5.99
HAUNTED LIVERPOOL 5	Tom Slemen	£5.99
HAUNTED LIVERPOOL 6	Tom Slemen	£5.99
HAUNTED LIVERPOOL 7	Tom Slemen	£5.99
HAUNTED LIVERPOOL 8	Tom Slemen	£5.99
HAUNTED LIVERPOOL 9	Tom Slemen	£5.99
HAUNTED LIVERPOOL 10	Tom Slemen	£5.99
HAUNTED LIVERPOOL 11	Tom Slemen	£5.99
HAUNTED LIVERPOOL 12	Tom Slemen	£5.99
HAUNTED LIVERPOOL 13	Tom Slemen	£5.99
HAUNTED LIVERPOOL 14	Tom Slemen	£5.99
STRANGE LIVERPOOL	Tom Slemen	£5.99
HAUNTED WIRRAL	Tom Slemen	£5.99
LIVERPOOL GHOST WALK	Tom Slemen	£5.99
HAUNTED CHESHIRE	Tom Slemen	£5.99
WICKED LIVERPOOL	Tom Slemen	£5.99
HAUNTED LIVERPOOL ANTHOLOGY	Tom Slemen	£6.99

HAUNTED LIVERPOOL double cassette audio book read by Tom Slemen £8.99

Available from all good bookshops

For a free stocklist contact:

THE BLUECOAT PRESS
329 Mariners House
Queens Dock Commercial Centre
Norfolk Street
Liverpool L1 0BG

Telephone: 0151 707 2390
Website: www.bluecoatpress.co.uk

If you have had a paranormal encounter, or a supernatural
experience of any sort, please drop a line to
Tom Slemen c/o the above address.